# An Approach to Modern Physics

Professor Edward Neville da Costa Andrade was born in 1887 and educated at St. Dunstan's College, University College (London), the University of Heidelberg, Cavendish Laboratory (Cambridge), and the University of Manchester. His books include *The Structure of the Atom, The Mechanism of Nature* (with Julian Huxley), *Simple Science, The New Chemistry, The Atom and Its Energy, Poems and Songs, Isaac Newton;* he has written as well numerous articles for various technical journals and the Encyclopaedia Britannica.

This book was originally published in 1956 by G. Bell and Sons, Ltd., London, England.

# AN APPROACH TO
# MODERN PHYSICS

### E. N. da C. Andrade
**D.SC., PH.D., LL.D., F.R.S.**

Doubleday Anchor Books
Doubleday & Company, Inc.
Garden City, New York, 1957

Cover by George Giusti

Typography by Edward Gorey

*Reprinted by arrangement with G. Bell and Sons, Ltd., London*

*Library of Congress Catalog Card Number 57–10448*

# Preface

IN 1930 I published, under the title of *The Mechanism of Nature*, a book which attempted to set out in simple form the fundamental facts and theories of physics. It was written primarily for readers who had not undergone any systematic training in science, though not without the modest hope that, in these days of narrow specialization, it might have interest for some scientists in their less strenuous moments. The little work was received with kindness and in 1936 a revised and extended fifth edition appeared. Since that date it has been frequently reprinted in unaltered form.

The past twenty years or so have seen such advances in physical science that a new reprint would give a very defective and unbalanced picture of the present situation. The vast developments in all matters concerning the behaviour of the atom and its nucleus at once come to mind, as exemplified by the investigations carried out with the great particle accelerators and by intensive research on cosmic rays, but these are by no means the only important innovations. Radiotelescopes and their revelations, radiocarbon dating, developments of the electron microscope and of supersonics exemplify matters that call for comment. Further, the fundamentals of physical thought have been much influenced by the general development of wave mechanics and by an increasing realization of the wider significance of the uncertainty principle originally put forward by Heisenberg.

It was clear, then, that if the position of physics to-day was to be presented in outline, very considerable additions would be needed. When I set about preparing the new matter I found that revision of much in the chapters retained from the older book was involved. The consequence is that what now appears is nearly twice as long as the old book and retains comparatively little of it in unaltered form. It was suggested to me, in particular by American friends, that the old title did not convey to the average prospective reader a correct notion of what was to be found between the covers and that the new book should be endowed with a title more precise and descriptive.

I mentioned in my preface of March 1930 that I had originally intended to call the book 'A Brief Introduction to Natural Philosophy', but felt that this title might give the misleading impression that it was mainly, in the sense usual to-day, a philosophical disquisition. I have now chosen a title which, by substituting the modern 'physics' for the old 'natural philosophy', avoids this incertitude. What it is wished to suggest is that from a simple account of the basic facts and theories of the older, now often called classical, physics, which still remain of fundamental importance, an approach is made to a description of physics as it is to-day. The experimental findings have made necessary and inevitable new conceptions and an attempt is made to show how new experimental methods and the results revealed by them have given rise to new theories.

In the final chapter the present position of the physics of the ultimate observable is discussed, together with what the author, and many others, hold to be its general philosophical implications. Here I have made every effort to represent fairly the situation, but I realize that, while far from seeking a brawl, I have ventured into a field where thwacks are not to be avoided. All that I can hope is that I have not deserved them and that I shall be left sufficiently sound to make a grateful bow towards any indulgent enough to approve what is here set before them.

I am much indebted to Professor H. S. W. Massey for having read and passed Chapter IX and to Professor C. F. Powell for having done the same in respect of what is written of cosmic rays. It is a pleasure to thank them for very helpful comment.

The sources of various photographs used for the plates are acknowledged under the individual pictures, but I should like to express here my gratitude for the permission, so freely accorded, to reproduce them.

E. N. DA C. ANDRADE

London
February 1956

... experience, it is a pleasure to acknowledge the very helpful hints of ...

The works of the ... search used for the ... are acknowledged and ... the various prepared in handbook ... to check the ... minute for the ... as ... they are used in each of them.

... H. ... G. ...

OHIO
February 19...

# CONTENTS

CONTENTS

# CHAPTER I

## What Is Physics?

*La physique cherche dans son domaine à reconstruire le monde, à le déduire par voie purement syllogistique d'un principe général une fois admis.* BOUASSE

IT is the task of the philosopher to reflect upon the general nature of the happenings, material and spiritual, that make up the life of man, and to endeavour to work out some scheme which shall help to reconcile conflicting appearances and simplify, by the investigation of first principles, the complex tangle of events in which our being is involved. It is for him to try to find some kind of an answer to the eternal 'Why?' which mankind, bewildered by the problems of good and evil, of life and death, has been uttering, now in the stammer of childhood, now in the harsh voice of agony, now in the quiet tones of reflecting age, since man has been a thinking animal. The nature of appearance and reality, the meaning of truth and falsehood, the scope and implication of our knowledge, the significance of the conception of beauty—these are among the hard questions on which the philosopher must exercise his powers. They are very wide and very elusive, difficult to enunciate satisfactorily, more difficult to solve in the least particular. New points of view can be found, but how are we to judge when a real advance has been made?

The task of the man of science is more modest: it is not

to answer the everlasting 'Why?' but the no less everlasting 'How?' He deals with the facts of observation, and tries to reduce them into a system, so that, if we admit certain principles to start with, things which are actually known to happen systematically can be shown to follow as necessary consequences, and a method of looking for new ones is suggested. The principles themselves are chosen to suit the facts, which for the man of science are all-important—*les principes ne se démontrent pas*. Whether the principles are in the absolute sense true is not a matter on which the man of science, as such, feels called to argue: if their consequences agree with Nature they are true enough to be useful, at any rate. The fundamental principles of science are, therefore, often called *working hypotheses*, since they are devised with the sole purpose of furnishing a basis upon which a system may be built corresponding in appearance with the behaviour of the material world, wherever we are able to make measurements or observations for comparison. We consider that an advance has been made when a wider range of the phenomena which are observed has been brought within the scope of one general principle.

It follows that a scientific theory may be abandoned when it has proved itself insufficient without in any way weakening the general worth of the scientific method. Let us consider for a moment the history of the atomic theory, as an example.[1] Sixty years ago it was generally held that atoms were hard, unbreakable entities, something like exceedingly minute billiard-balls, each element possessing a perfectly definite type of atom, fundamentally different from that of any other element. This belief, this hypothesis, was sufficient to explain the properties of gases, for by supposing that atoms of this kind possessed certain motions obeying the laws of mechanics, results could be deduced mathematically which agreed excellently with the properties of gases as they were observed in the laboratory. By endowing such atoms

[1] The atomic theory is discussed in Chapter VIII, where any unfamiliar terms receive further explanation.

with certain forces of attraction, or affinities, the general facts of chemistry could be explained.

Then came the discovery of the electron, which is very much lighter than any atom, and suggested the possibility that the different types of atom might be built up of electrons. Further, the discovery of radio-activity showed that certain atoms, such as those of elements of the radium family, could fire off electrically charged particles, and so not only contained those particles as parts of their structure, but also must possess within themselves a certain store of energy, to provide the energy which the radiations carried away. It was a question of either admitting the existence of this internal energy or of denying the principle of the conservation of energy, for the radio-active elements give out energy without any energy being put into them by us.

The principle of the conservation of energy had proved too generally useful to be given up, although it was definitely suggested by some that it would have to be abandoned. The facts of radio-activity forced us, however, to abandon the idea that the atom was unbreakable, or anything like a minute billiard-ball, for the atoms of a radio-active element shoot off fragments of themselves and become atoms of other elements. Results of further researches could only be explained by supposing that the atom had a structure like a minute solar system, the mass of the atom being concentrated in an excessively small nucleus at the centre, and the rest of the atom consisting of electrons with wide spaces between them. This picture of the atom is discussed later in this book, and something is said of the great changes which it, in its turn, has undergone to make it fit in with the astonishing results of recent experiment and observation. What has just been said is sufficient, perhaps, to show how great a change in our ideas on this subject has taken place within two generations.

Is the critic, then, justified in reproaching the physicist in this way: *Sixty years ago you told us that atoms were hard, indivisible, and unbreakable, made perfect in the beginning of things, and persisting in unworn perfection ever since.*

*To-day you tell us that atoms are loose structures which can be very easily broken: you speak of radio-active atoms breaking up and changing to simpler atoms, and with your cyclotrons and what not you not only manufacture from one kind of known atom other kinds of known atom, but even new, hitherto unknown, kinds of atom. You tell us that the manufacture and breakdown of atoms is an essential part of the mechanism of the heavens. What are we to believe? Your accepted theories of one generation are abandoned in the next: how can I be sure that you are right this time?* In my opinion, the correct answer is that we do not claim any absolute truth for our theories: we claim, rather, that a theory like our modern atomic theory has very great merits because most of the phenomena with which we are at present acquainted are just such as we should expect if it were true.

Nature, in the aspects which the physicist investigates, behaves *as if* there were atoms and *as if* they had the properties which we now claim for them. The older conception of atoms was good enough to explain the phenomena then considered, and we can still use it for certain simpler problems, where introducing the idea of atomic structure brings in needless complications; but to explain the facts of atomic change and atomic radiations we must introduce the newer forms of the atomic theory. We do not claim any finality for the theory: some new discovery may suddenly force us to modify our ideas in many particulars, some new discoverer may show that certain complications can be simplified with advantage, but the successes of the present theory show that we shall probably have to retain many of its general features. It is an excellent working hypothesis because it has shown us law where law was not hitherto discovered, and connections between different phenomena where before we knew of no connection. It has enabled us to arrange our known facts in a more convenient and logical way, and has pointed the way to the discovery of very interesting new facts. It is justified by its works, but it is not final. Science is a living thing, and living things develop.

Some people might be inclined to go further, and claim a definite reality for atoms, electrons, and other ultimate particles, and for the scheme of atomic structure which has been worked out. The great point is that whether the man of science regards his atoms as having an ultimate reality or not does not affect the validity of the theory: the theory is just as useful in introducing order and promoting discovery if they are merely polite fictions as if they are desperate realities, and two men who hold different views on this point will both, if they are equally adequate as mathematicians and equally capable as physicists, be able to make the same predictions based on the theory, and to derive the same satisfaction from the experimental verification. To take a simple illustration: two different men may hold different views of a given politician, one holding that he is paid by a certain interest to act in a certain way, and the other believing in his integrity. If, however, he always behaves *as if* he were paid by that interest; if all his actions hitherto can be explained on that basis, and the way he will vote on any particular matter can be successfully predicted on this assumption; then he who is to represent the attitude of the man of science in our parable will say: 'It is impossible for me to find out whether he is paid or not, but because all his actions can be explained on the theory that he is, I will adopt it. It economizes thought, in that this one working hypothesis enables me to understand all the happenings connected with the man's career. As a realist I do not greatly care whether it is true or not. I do not judge: I observe and classify my observations and I use them to predict what will happen in given circumstances.' The moralist, who represents the attitude of the philosopher, will, however, be greatly exercised as to the existence or not of the bribes, and will be quite without any means of going behind the scenes to find out. He will merely be able to speculate. It is a more delicate problem, but one where no final solution can be reached.

On this view, any particular scientific theory is a provisional tool with which we carve knowledge of the material world out of the block of Nature. It may at any moment be supplanted by an improved version or by a completely new theory, but this is only to say that when we get a better tool, which does all that this one does and something more as well, we will abandon our present tool. To refuse to use a tool because some day a better one may be invented is folly: in the same way, not to make use of a theory which has been proved capable of explaining a great many facts, and of suggesting new lines of research, because it has acknowledged flaws, and is incapable of explaining other facts, would be folly. To use another metaphor, the history of science may, as has been said, be full of beautiful theories slain by ugly little facts, but those theories did not die in vain if before their death they had subdued a vast number of jarring facts into a law-abiding populace. Nor do theories generally die a final death: often they are resurrected with some new feature which gets over the old difficulty.

The difference, then, between any religious belief and a scientific theory is that the former has for the believers an element of absolute truth: it is a standard by which they stand or fall, and to abandon it is dishonour and sin. The scientific theory is, however, only true as long as it is useful. The man of science regards even his best theory as a makeshift device to help him on his way, and is always on the lookout for something better and more comprehensive.

To emphasize the pragmatic nature of scientific hypothesis the contrast between physics and philosophy has here been put in the most extreme way. Some philosophers, of the school of William James, take the view that, when we say that a belief is true, all we mean is that it is useful—that all truth is justified by experience, and in no other way, just as a scientific theory is. In any case, the true philosopher cannot, of course, neglect the methods and findings of science, bearing as they do on the nature of knowledge and the character of inductive reasoning. On the other hand, the physicist is bound to feel interest in investigating the character of his assumptions from the point of view of the logician. In the old days the term philosophy was used in the most general sense, and what we now call physics was termed natural philosophy (a term still used in Scotland, and one that might well be revived) as distinct from moral philosophy. Remembering this, the purport of what has already been written is well summed up in a sentence of the great mathematical physicist Fourier: *'Les causes primordiales ne nous sont pas connues; mais elles sont assujetties à des lois simples et constantes, que l'on peut découvrir par l'observation, et dont l'étude est l'objet de la philosophie naturelle'.*[2]

So far we have spoken of science as a whole, although we have had in mind particularly the science of inanimate matter, in which the specific characteristics of science are, perhaps, more strongly emphasized than in the biological sciences, in that more exact methods and measurements are possible. In such sciences as astronomy and physics the hypotheses are put into a form adapted for precise mathematical expression, and their consequences can be deduced with the rigorousness of mathematical reasoning. We are not content with predicting that something will happen: we require formulae which will enable us to calculate the exact magnitude of the effect to be anticipated, and our observations or experiments consist in precise measurements which we can compare, figure against figure, with the results given by the theory. Thus in astronomy we are not content with knowing that the planets go round the sun; we must have a theory which will enable us to deduce the exact paths of the planets, and of comets, taking into account the disturbances which one planet experiences from the action of the others. The decision between Newton's and Einstein's system of mechanics can only be made by close calculation of the consequences of the two theories in certain extreme cases, where a slight numerical difference is in question: we ask Nature, by meticulous measurement, which is right, and abide by her decision.

The modern theories of the atom carry their conviction

---

[2] The primordial causes are not known to us, but they are subjected to laws of a simple and unvarying nature, which can be discovered by observation: the study of these laws is the object of natural philosophy.

by virtue of the convincing closeness with which their mathematical consequences agree with measurements made with, for instance, spectrometers. During the First World War certain ingenious gentlemen, knowing that magnets attract iron and steel, suggested that submarines should be drawn to the shore by huge magnets. It is true that a large magnet will exert a force on a submarine, but the laws of magnetic attraction are precise, and allow us to calculate in a moment that the effect of even the largest conceivable artificial magnet will be far too small to effect this fanciful consummation, even at a small distance. Calculation decides. The first impulse of the physicist in devising an experiment is to try to calculate the magnitude of the effect to be expected, so as to see if it is measurable, and every advance in theory is based upon a number of painstaking measurements made by previous workers. The theory of relativity itself, although a complete logical structure, arose from the fruitless search for an experimental verification of a very, very small effect predicted by previous theories.

We must now try to indicate the particular scope of the science of physics, or, rather, its relation to the other exact sciences. Physics deals with the material aspect of the inanimate world, and is particularly concerned with processes in which the nature of the matter is unchanged. If the nature of the matter changes, as when copper and sulphuric acid form copper sulphate, the study belongs to the science of chemistry. Endeavouring to be more specific, we may say that the measured properties of lifeless matter involving no change of chemical composition, and of energy and radiation, in all their many forms, are the particular province of physics. Text-books usually group the subject under the headings: properties of matter (which includes such subjects as gravity, elasticity, friction of all kinds, and various liquid properties, such as surface tension); heat; light; sound; electricity and magnetism. This division is a very arbitrary one, and what we are to include under each head is also very arbitrary. Physics, endeavouring to find out exact laws for the behaviour of matter and radiation, is the most fundamental of the experimental sciences,[3] as it is the most precise and mathematical, and has its part in all the others: as they tend to become more exact they tend to come more and more within the scope of physics. The way in which physics mingles with the other sciences can be briefly illustrated by a few examples.

Mathematics is, of course, involved in every branch of physics, and, in return, physical investigation into such subjects as the conduction of heat have led to new methods in applied mathematics. Geometry, especially geometry other than that of Euclid, is deeply involved in the theory of relativity. The determination of the forces of gravity, which lies within the province of physics, is of great importance for astronomy. Astrophysics, which is the science of determining the atomic constitution and physical behaviour of the heavenly bodies, in particular the sun, is merely the application of earthly physics to heavenly ends. In such parts of chemistry as the electrical and optical properties of different substances, and in considerations of the rates at which chemical changes take place, physics is so heavily involved that a special branch of science is called physical chemistry, while in organic chemistry the application of X-rays, by methods developed in physics, has produced important results bearing on the grouping, and arrangement in space, of atoms in the molecules of organic compounds. Quite apart from this, however, it is now clearly recognized that the forces of chemical combination are electrical in nature, so that physics is now playing a leading part in chemistry. In general, the borderland between physics and chemistry is so wide and so indefinite that it is often pointless to discuss whether a particular problem is one of physics or of chemistry.

Crystallography—and hence mineralogy—is deeply indebted to the X-ray analysis of crystal structure. In geology the question of the age of the earth is one on which physics

[3] By saying experimental sciences, I except astronomy, which is observational but not strictly experimental, and, of course, mathematics, which is fundamental to physics.

has much to say, radio-activity in particular having thrown light on this subject. In botany and in medicine physical methods are becoming more and more necessary: in fact in recent years the special name of biophysics has been given to the branch of science which applies the methods and instruments of physics to the study of living things. Even in philology, the science of speech, physics enters in connection with the study of vowel sounds, which involves the question of the resonance of the cavities of the mouth and throat, and such-like studies. Meteorology, the science of the weather, depends for all her results on physics, particularly in connection with atmospheric electricity in all its aspects, including the electrical effects connected with the growth and division of raindrops. A new science of the physics of the earth (or geophysics, as some prefer to call it) treats of such subjects as terrestrial magnetism, earthquake propagation, and the aurora borealis. The practical applications of physics in engineering and electrical engineering are so multifarious that mention is impossible, and so familiar that it is unnecessary. The method of physics is finding new scope and success every year, and the instruments invented and perfected by physics—the microscope, the telescope, the spectrometer, the hot-wire valve, the cathode-ray oscillograph, the Geiger counter, and a host of others—are constantly extending their field of usefulness.

From the point of view of physics we know something about a thing when we can measure it precisely, and find exact relations between it and other things which can be brought under the scope of our few fundamental principles. Thus we know something about the capacity for heat of different materials—that is, we can measure the amount of heat which is required to raise the temperature of a unit weight of a substance by one degree, which is called the specific heat if we take water as a standard. It is a precise quantity for each definite kind of matter. We also know that the specific heat is connected fundamentally with the elasticity of the body, and with its chemical composition. But, from the point of view of physics, we know comparatively little of plasticity, the property which renders clay so valuable to the potter. The potter or the sculptor can tell by touch and experience whether a clay is in a suitable state for working, but science has not yet found a precise way of measuring this suitability: we do not yet know how to test a clay, and allot a definite figure of merit—a coefficient of plasticity, let us say—so that we could say that one clay was, for instance, 1.49 times as plastic, in this sense, as another. Consequently, we do not know much of the connection between plasticity and other properties. Measurement is the beginning of physical knowledge.

From what has been said, it is clear that we must have certain conceptions and laws which we take as fundamental, just as in a game there are certain fundamental rules. If someone asks why it is a fault at lawn tennis if the player's foot is not behind the baseline at the moment of serving, the only possible answer is that that is the way the game is played: the question is a meaningless one if by it the questioner means that he wants an explanation in terms of international law or police regulations. But the question, 'What is electricity?'—so often asked—is just as meaningless, and, to do them justice, the questioners have probably never thought at all about the kind of answer they require. Electricity is one of the fundamental conceptions of physics: it is absurd to expect to be told that it is a kind of liquid, or a known kind of force, when we explain the properties of liquids in terms of electricity, and electric force is perhaps the fundamental conception of modern physics. The physicist can tell you what he means by an electric charge: he will say that when bodies are in a certain state they repel or attract one another in certain ways, and that then, as a quick way of describing that state, he speaks of the bodies as electrically charged. He can tell you the properties of these charges at rest and in motion: the connection between moving charges and magnetism: the circumstances in which there is a flow of electrical energy: how electrical energy can be converted into other forms of energy: and a thousand such things about electricity. In short, the correct question is, 'What does electricity?' not, 'What is electricity?' The former has a definite meaning, and can be answered: the latter is not a fair question in that the questioner does not really formulate his inquiry in such a way as to convey what he wants to know. If he means 'Can you express what you know about electricity in terms of something more fundamental?' the answer is definitely 'No. We must have in physics something behind which we do not go: if it were not electricity, it would have to be some other conception.'

Now that we have briefly considered the kind of knowledge which physics is, we can discuss, very briefly, some of the general results of the science.

## CHAPTER II

### About Heat and Energy

CONSIDERATIONS of energy enter into every branch of physics—in fact, a good case could be made out for defining physics as the study of energy and its transformation. The conception of energy in its general form was, however, of comparatively late development, for the principle of the conservation of energy was not clearly enunciated until 1847. Let us see what it implies.

When a body moves under the influence of a force we say that work is done, and we measure the work done by multiplying the force in the direction of motion by the distance moved through: engineers, for instance, measure work done in foot-pounds.[1] If any agent possesses the power of doing work we say that it possesses energy, and we measure the change of energy by the work done.

Now, mechanical energy, possessed by a solid or a liquid or a gas, may be of two kinds, that which a body possesses in virtue of its motion, the so-called kinetic energy, and that which it possesses in virtue of its position, the so-called potential energy. The wind, for instance, possesses energy by virtue of the motion of the air: it can drive a windmill, which does work. The air before passing the mill-sail is moving faster than the air as it issues from the sail on the other side. It has lost speed, and the loss of energy of motion ap-

[1] More correctly, foot-pounds-weight, since the force is the pull of gravity on the pound.

pears largely as the work which the mill is set to do. In the same way with the water turbine the stream of water loses speed in passing through the turbine wheels: in the steam turbine the steam pressure is used to create a steam wind which loses energy of motion to produce the work done by the engine.

On the other hand, in a clock the energy which drives it is derived from position. In the old type of weight-driven clock the weights were high up when the clock was wound, and lost this energy of position as the force of gravity slowly pulled them down: the clock spring likewise possesses energy when coiled, which it loses as it moves under the influence of the stresses set up in the spring when it is wound. In a switchback railway the car when ready to start has a store of energy in virtue of its position at the top of the run.

Now it is quite clear that kinetic energy can be converted into potential energy. The switchback railway (or helter-skelter lighthouse, or any other fair-ground fantasies on the old theme) gives us a particularly good example of this conversion. As the car falls it gathers speed, the speed increasing until it reaches the lowest point of its run, when its potential energy is least: as it climbs again, and gains potential energy, it loses kinetic energy. If there were no friction it would climb again just to the height at which it started, at which point it would have lost all its speed and just cease crawling, but in practice the first hump, at the top of which it nearly stops, is always lower than the starting-point. Since at this point it has practically lost all its kinetic energy gained on the run down, and has less potential energy than that with which it started, a certain amount of energy has apparently been lost. This energy is the energy required to push the car against the frictional forces set up at the rails and axles and so on, but more particularly against the resistance offered by the air to rapid motion. We seem, however, to have nothing to show for it. The clear realization of the history of this lost energy was one of the most important turning-points in nineteenth-century physics.

That kinetic energy could be turned into potential energy,

and *vice versa,* was recognized in the early days of mechanics as an exact science: the great advance embodied in the enunciation of the conservation of energy was that heat is a form of energy, and that, when mechanical energy apparently disappears by friction, heat is generated. It is a familiar fact that badly lubricated bearings, where friction is high, get very hot, and that the harder it is to keep the parts moving in their bearings the hotter the bearings get; but in general the heat generated at bearings is small and escapes notice. A weight falls to the ground, gaining energy of motion, but this motion disappears when the weight reaches the floor. It actually reappears as heat, the weight, and the floor at the point of impact, becoming slightly warmer, but the amount of energy in question does not represent sufficient heat to be easily detectable. There are, however, cases where the amount of heat is surprisingly large. At Portsmouth Dockyard there used to be—and probably is still—a machine which stamped large rivet-holes in very thick steel plates. The amount of work done in forcing the die through the plate must naturally be very large. It used to be a favourite trick for the workman operating the machine to pick up in his horny hand the plug of metal as it fell to the floor and hand it to the curious visitor, who at once dropped it, to the delight of his friends, for the plug was exceedingly hot. The energy had been conserved—as heat.

It was the great service of Joule to prove the exact equivalence of heat and mechanical work: that wherever mechanical work apparently disappears, not only is heat generated, but an amount of heat exactly proportional to the energy that seems lost. The work can be done in various ways: by rubbing pieces of metal together, or by stirring water, or—what is important for us—electrically, by pushing electric charges through a wire by electromotive force, or, in more usual words, by passing an electric current through a resistance.

The work done in stirring water in the ordinary way—say in stirring a cup of coffee—is, of course, very small, and consequently no appreciable amount of heat is generated:

stirring the hot coffee actually makes it cooler, because fresh layers of hot liquid are brought into contact with the cold air and further evaporation is encouraged. If, however, complicated paddles are used, in conjunction with vanes protruding from the side of the vessel, it can be made quite difficult to move the paddles and, corresponding to the greater work done, larger quantities of heat are generated, which can be accurately measured. It is interesting to note that when J. R. Mayer, who, round about 1842, was one of the earliest to realize the equivalence of heat and work, was explaining his idea, his friend Jolly objected: 'But in that case water ought to get warmer if you shake it', which appeared to him absurd. Mayer left without saying a word, but entered his friend's room some weeks later with the words: 'So it does', assuming that his friend, like himself, had been thinking of nothing else since. He had turned to experiment: he had asked Nature to decide. The celebrated Rowland,[2] in a most accurate and laborious research on the quantity of heat produced by a measured amount of energy used in stirring water, often raised the temperature of the water by more than 20° C, and Reynolds and Moorby raised water to boiling-point by churning it.

Heat, then, is a form of energy, and not only is work turned into heat at all places where there is friction, including in this term the 'friction' of electricity passing through

[2] H. A. Rowland, of Johns Hopkins University, Baltimore, was a great character. It is told of him—how correctly I cannot vouch—that when he was appearing as expert witness in a law case, he was asked, in the course of cross-examination, 'Who is, at the present time, the greatest authority on scientific matters in the States', to which he replied 'I am'. After the hearing a friend indicated that to some this reply might possibly seem to savour of vanity, to which he observed gravely, 'Possibly, but you must remember that I was on oath'. He was a close friend of Clerk Maxwell, who in his light verse alludes to him as 'Rowland of Troy, that doughty knight', and says, for instance,

'  'Twas when Sir Rowland, as a stage
        From Troy to Baltimore, took root
     In Berlin . . .'

a wire (a process clearly visible in the electric lamp or electric radiator), but heat can be turned into work. In every steam-engine there is an actual disappearance of heat corresponding to the energy represented by the work done. If all the heat generated by the furnace is measured, and allowances made for the heat given to the condenser water, not as much heat is gained by the surroundings as if the same amount of fuel were burnt without driving an engine.

There are many forms of energy. Sound can be reckoned as mechanical energy, as explained in Chapter III. Light, together with radiations of all kinds, such as X-rays or wireless waves, is also a form of energy. The energy of radiation is generally measured as heat, which is but another example of the way in which the conception of heat as a form of energy pervades all modern physics. Suppose, for instance, that it is required to measure the energy of, let us suppose, a red light of a certain wave-length. The light is made to fall on a strip of blackened metal, which absorbs it practically completely, for no appreciable light is thrown back. The energy of the light is transformed into heat, and correspondingly the strip grows warmer, the slight rise in temperature being measured by delicate electrical methods. The amount of heat which would be required to produce the rise of temperature being calculated, the equivalent energy is the energy of the light. The energy of an infra-red radiation or of a wireless wave can be measured in a similar way by the heating effect.

The energy of mechanical motion can always be converted into heat, and such conversion is going on all round us in Nature. At the foot of a waterfall, where the downward rush of the water is checked and dissipated in whirlpools and turbulence, the energy of motion is replaced by a slight heating of the water: the water of the storm-lashed sea is warmer than that of the tranquil ocean, other things being equal: the falling meteor, which is a cold lump during its passage through empty space, becomes glowing hot as its very rapid motion is checked on entering the earth's atmosphere. Under certain conditions the reverse process—the change of heat into work—can take place, but only under certain conditions. That the occasions on which this conversion can take place are limited does not contradict what we have said about a given quantity of work always being equivalent to a fixed quantity of heat: the fact that we can only buy bread at certain hours and at certain shops does not affect the price of bread being fixed when we can buy it. The rate of exchange for the conversion of heat into work is fixed: whether, and how far, the conversion can be effected depends upon circumstances.

The relations between heat and work are the subject of the science of thermodynamics, which means literally the science of heat-power. It is the peculiarity of the thermodynamic method that it does not inquire as to the nature of heat—that is, as to whether it is a motion of molecules, or something like the trembling of a jelly, or what else. In thermodynamics we are content to say that we can measure heat energy in various ways: that we have a conception of a state called temperature, which we can likewise define and measure: and that we can measure mechanical work. Our object is to find relations which govern the behaviour of the measured quantities. The first great relation is that which we have already mentioned: that a certain quantity of work is equivalent to a precise quantity of heat, no matter how that work be turned into heat. This is the first law of thermodynamics, and, if we seem to be stressing it overmuch, it must be pleaded in excuse that it really is a keystone of physics. It is a denial of the possibility of constructing a perpetual motion machine, for it tells us that we can only get energy out of a machine by supplying it with at least as much energy in some form or other, either mechanical energy or electrical energy or heat.

The law is, of course, nothing more than the embodiment of all our experience, but this means that every careful and authenticated observation agrees with it, and that every apparent exception proves on examination to be fallacious. The ordinary perpetual motion machines of crazy inventors are perfectly well-known types, often, however, requiring some little ingenuity to detect the false step in reasoning.

It is as profitable to organize an expedition to discover a place where weights fall upwards as to spend time planning machines of rods, levers, balls, pumps, cams, and such-like to produce energy by their mere motion.[3] Nobody can say that such a place may not exist somewhere on the earth's surface, in so far as there are still unexplored territories where the downfalling habits of weights have not yet been confirmed, but, if it does, then all the most stable parts of the structure of science are naught. Most of the inventors of perpetual motion machines (who, judging from my correspondence, still exist in numbers) are the victims of self-deception, but a certain number are shrewd gentlemen who collect money to float companies for exploiting their inventions. Finding, it would seem, that most people realize to-day that you cannot get energy out of nothing, these modern inventors have turned to producing machines by which a small supply of energy is ostensibly turned into a large one. This lends itself to very plausible pseudo-scientific explanations. It is, however, equally against the first law of thermodynamics, and equally futile.

This first law does not, however, tell us anything about the conditions necessary for the conversion of heat into work to take place. It might be, for all this law tells us, possible to set up a machine by the side of a lake, to draw heat from the water of the lake, and to turn that heat into work. If this could be done the lake would simply become colder than the surrounding country, and, corresponding to this abstraction of heat, we should be running our machinery just as well as if we had a stream turning a water turbine. The motion of a stream, however, serves to remind us that we cannot, from a lake, get a stream of water unless we have a place at a lower level for the water to flow to: if

---

[3] Those interested in the subject will find a full history of the various types of perpetual motion machine invented up to 1860 in Henry Dircks's *Perpetuum Mobile: or Search for Self-Motive Power*, 1861–70. The work is very scarce, especially the second volume, but is accessible in many of the more important libraries.

water is to be used for turning wheels it must be higher than its surroundings. Not only a body of water but a difference of water-levels is necessary for water power.

Precisely the same thing holds of a source of heat: for us to be able to convert any part of it into work the source of heat must be at a higher temperature than its surroundings. It is not only that we cannot use up the heat of ponds and lakes (I select bodies of water, because the heat capacity of water is much higher than that of stone, for instance, and because the circulation possible in water would help us to utilize the heat, if it were in any way possible to do so) and turn it into work: we could not use the heat of the furnace of a steam turbine if the whole of the engine-room were at the same temperature. We must have a condenser at a lower temperature than the furnace,[4] if we are to convert some of the heat of the furnace into work, and the bigger the difference of temperature between the boiler and the condenser, the larger the fraction of the heat which we can turn into work. This is why to-day great efforts are being made to use steam at higher and higher pressure: the higher the pressure of the steam the higher the temperature, and the greater the efficiency. Steam in itself can do nothing: on a hot planet all the water would be steam, but no steam-engine could be run, for lack of a condenser.

The second law of thermodynamics implies this property of heat, that we cannot convert it into work unless we have a difference of temperatures, and that the bigger this difference the bigger the fraction we can utilize, the fraction not utilized remaining, of course, as heat, since there can be no loss of energy as a whole. It tells us, in terms of the temperatures in question, exactly what heat energy is convertible. The applications in engineering are obvious, but the law has such general importance that it is widely applied in physics and chemistry, and, if used with due caution, can be applied to the universe. It must, however, be used with

---

[4] In the case of a non-condensing engine, like an old-fashioned locomotive, the surrounding air acts as the lower temperature.

great caution, and here we have an excellent example of the nature of a physical theory which is constructed for dealing with certain classes of problems, and often cannot be used outside those problems. The laws of thermodynamics are, in their essence, average laws—that is, we have no reason to suppose that they are true of single atoms, or of small assemblies of atoms, for we never consider anything but pieces of matter containing millions of millions of millions of atoms when making the heat measurements on which these laws are based.

A refreshment caterer might work out his requirements on the basis that every thousand men eat so many sausages, so many doughnuts, and so on, and might find that those calculations were always satisfactory. They would, however, tell him nothing about what the single men eat: how many eat nothing, how many eat more than their share, how many eat only sausages. If he wanted to calculate for a crowd in a different part of the country it might suit him better to study the behaviour of the single man under different conditions, and from that construct the needs of the crowd. This corresponds to the other method of studying heat problems to which we now turn—namely the atomic method. It has the disadvantage, compared to the thermodynamic method, that it demands a more detailed knowledge to begin with: for engineering purposes, for instance, where we know that the thermodynamic method is in general sufficient, it would lead to unnecessary complications to consider the behaviour of atoms. On the other hand, it has the great advantage that, if we can get the necessary knowledge, we get an insight into the working of the machine of Nature which enables us to go behind the general effects and to examine the medley of minute complications of which these general effects are the visible result.

From the point of view of the atomic theory, we can at once say that heat energy is nothing but the energy of motion (to which must be added in some cases the potential energy) of the molecules of which matter is composed. Let us consider a gas, for instance. It consists of molecules, more complex in some gases, less complex in others, but in all cases about a hundred-millionth of an inch across, with comparatively large spaces between, moving about in all directions with an average speed measured in hundreds of yards a second. The molecules collide with one another, and lose or gain in speed at collision, so that all velocities from very small to very great are represented. Individual molecules, therefore, will have very different kinetic energies of straight-line motion, but at a definite temperature, if several million of them are considered, there will be a certain definite average kinetic energy. The molecules will also be set rotating by the collisions, and will have an energy of spin, like tops or like shells fired from a gun, which spin and move forward at the same time, except that the molecule may be spinning round an axis set in *any* direction.

The molecules consist in general of atoms held together by electric forces, and the atoms may also vibrate, as if the molecule were made of balls joined together by springs, so that the molecule can possess kinetic and potential energy of vibration, like a pendulum. In short, every molecule possesses a certain amount of what we may call mechanical energy of various kinds. The hotter the gas the more lively is the motion of its molecules, or, more precisely put, the greater the average energy of the molecules. The actual process of heating can be imagined thus: the molecules of the flame or hot body, with which we put the vessel containing our gas in contact, are in more energetic motion than those of the cold vessel, and by beating against these communicate some of their energy to them. The molecules of the vessel in turn strike vigorously the gas molecules as they come in contact with them, until they too gain in energy. If the vessel be closed the more lively beating of the gas molecules against its sides produces the rise in pressure which we know takes place when a gas is heated in a sealed space.

In a liquid we likewise have energy of motion of the molecule, but it is not so simple to analyse, since, whereas in a gas the molecules have comparatively long, straight paths between the collisions, in a liquid they are so crowded together that the motion is controlled by the forces of the neighbouring molecules. In a solid the molecules are anchored to definite spots by the forces of cohesion, and vibrate about that spot like balls held by springs. In all cases, however, the heat energy is simply the energy involved in different modes in the motion of the molecules.

This motion of the molecules is a random motion. If we could fix our eyes on a given molecule, and follow its career, we should see it moving now in one direction, now in a totally unrelated direction, and if we could throw a glimpse at all the molecules at once, we should see that different molecules were moving in different directions. Instead of behaving like well-drilled soldiers, they resemble an aimless crowd. Contrast this with what we do when we push a piece of matter from one place to another, say, for instance, when we slide a block of wood along a table. Every molecule in the block has now, as well as its irregular motion, a perfectly definite motion in a particular direction: the actual motion of a given molecule will, of course, be obtained by considering the joint effect of the common motion and of the irregular motion. We have, by moving the block as a whole, introduced an element of order into the motion. If we just give the block a push it soon comes to rest owing to friction, and we know that heat will be generated where it rubs along the table. This generation of heat means, as we have seen, a general increase in the irregular motion of the molecules in the neighbourhood of the surfaces where friction takes place. In other words, instead of saying that our mechanical energy has been converted into heat, we can say that the energy of the regular motion which we imposed on the molecules when we pushed the block has been converted into energy of irregular motion of the molecules. This represents a general tendency in Nature. Regularity of motion tends to disappear, and to be replaced by irregular molecular motion. Everything tends to 'mixed-uppedness'.

Let us consider a few examples. Suppose we have two bodies, at different temperatures, in a room—say a furnace and a tank of water. There is a class-distinction created by man: the molecules of gas in the furnace have on the average a greater energy than the molecules of water in the tank. If everything is left to itself the whole room will eventually come to one temperature: the fire in the furnace will have gone out and the furnace will have shared its heat with everything else in the room. A million molecules taken at one place will have exactly the same average energy as a million molecules at any other place. None of the heat energy has been turned into work.

When the furnace was hot and the tank cold, however, we could by an engine have converted a certain amount of the heat of the furnace into work: we could, say, have run a dynamo and charged accumulator cells which would then run one of the old-type electric cars for us. This is a regular co-ordinated motion, all molecules of the car having a common drift imposed on them. But what will have happened when we have run our car out and back home again? The accumulator will have run down, and we shall have nothing to show for our energy, being exactly where we started. Where has it gone? In friction of wheels on the road, of axles in their bearings, of chassis against the wind. All our regularity has vanished, to be replaced by the additional irregular motion consequent on the slight heating of road, bearings, and wind and chassis—very slight heating, except, perhaps, in the case of the bearings. Nature has won. We may say, then, that man represents a ceaseless struggle to impose an element of regularity useful to himself on the irregular molecular motion of the bodies that compose our world.

If we consider bodies of visible size, containing millions of millions of millions of molecules, we are led to exactly the same result whether we apply the gross laws of thermodynamics or the individual method of molecular physics. But suppose we consider molecules themselves, or very small particles. The molecules in a given piece of stuff are in perpetual motion: if the piece is at a high temperature the average motion is more vigorous than if it is at a low temperature. We know, however, that in the one piece of stuff some of the molecules will have a high degree of motion, the others very little: the temperature which we measure with a thermometer indicates an average only. Suppose we could pick out all the little, inconceivably little, bits where the molecules were in vigorous motion, and put them in one place, and all the little bits where the molecules were comparatively quiet, and put them in another place, we should have obtained from a body at one temperature, according to our thermometer, two pieces which thermometers would show to be at different temperatures.

To imagine how this might be done, suppose, as Clerk Maxwell[5] did, that we have a vessel of air, divided into two by a partition. In this partition is a minute hole with a sliding door, worked by a very intelligent microbe or, as Maxwell described the creature, 'a being whose faculties are so sharpened that he can follow every molecule in its course'. This being is usually called 'Maxwell's demon'. When he sees a fast molecule coming from right to left he opens his door and lets it through: when he sees a slow molecule coming from left to right he lets that through. Soon he will have all his energetic molecules on the left, all the sluggish ones on the right. There will be, of course, a redistribution of energy among the molecules in each compartment, but, on the whole, the energy in the compartment to which only fast molecules were admitted will be greater than that in the other. The temperature will be correspondingly higher in the one compartment than in the other. The microbe need have done no work, for his door can be imagined as light and as well lubricated as we like. Therefore, from a body at one temperature we have, without doing work, obtained bodies at two different temperatures, with which we can work a little engine. It is, however, against the second law of thermodynamics for us to be able to obtain work

[5] Clerk Maxwell was one of the greatest intellects of the past century, to whom in particular the original theory of electromagnetic waves and much fundamental work on the molecular theory of gases are due.

from a body originally all at one temperature. What is the explanation?

The explanation is simply that the laws of thermodynamics only apply to visible pieces of matter, and that they suppose that we cannot employ beings who can follow the movements of single molecules. If we could drill and discipline molecules, if we could, without doing work, interfere with the 'mixed-uppedness' of Nature, we could violate the law—but we cannot so interfere. If the caterer, whom we cited before, could go and talk to each individual man in his crowd of thousands, no doubt he could influence the demand for particular viands in any way he liked. As it is, he must arrange his supplies to suit what he knows to be the bulk demand of a large crowd. Our ordinary laws of physics, engineering, and chemistry are laws for the behaviour of immense crowds of molecules.

When we come to think of things in terms of molecules we have to introduce probability instead of certainty. Suppose I put a coin on the table. The millions of millions of millions of molecules of the table-top under it are moving at random—some fast, some slow, some up, some down, and the coin stays put. If, however, owing to chance fluctuations, it so happened that at a particular instant a large excess of particles were to be moving upwards and at the same time a correspondingly smaller number of particles moving downwards, then the coin would be hammered upwards—it would jump. Is it impossible that there should be an appreciable momentary increase of pressure produced by molecular bombardment of the coin? Is it impossible that a penny fairly tossed shall come down heads six thousand times or more in ten thousand tosses? The answer in both cases is, 'No, not impossible, but very, very, very improbable'. Actually, in the case of the penny, it requires a number with eighty-seven zeros to express how improbable it is: a million million to one chance is exceedingly likely compared to it. Practically, we may just as well say that it *is* impossible, but philosophically there is a difference. Thermodynamics says bluntly: 'Impossible' in such cases.

Our citation of coin-tossing suggests a further step. Suppose we toss only a hundred times: is it so wildly improbable that there will be sixty heads or more? No, it is only thirty-three to one against. And suppose we toss only ten times: the chance of six heads, or more, is quite large, only about 2 to 1 against. In the same way, suppose we take a very minute particle, of, say, about a thousand times the diameter of a single molecule, floating in the interior of a liquid or a gas, we can calculate what is the chance that the force of the molecular blows which it receives on one side may exceed the force of the blows which it receives on the other side sufficiently to produce a perceptible movement. The result of the calculation is that with a particle of the size in question, which can be seen with a high-power microscope, we should expect a small irregular movement, big enough to be perceived by the microscope, due to the agitation of the molecules with which it is surrounded. The smaller the grain the livelier the agitation to be anticipated. On the other hand, the chance of appreciable movement of any grain that can be easily seen by the naked eye, in a liquid protected from currents, is so exceedingly small that it is hopeless to try to observe it.

It appears, then, that if our conception of heat as molecular energy were true we should be able to see, as it were, a slow-motion picture of this agitation in the irregular movement of microscopic grains suspended in a liquid. As a matter of fact, such a movement was discovered long before its theoretical meaning was realized. About a hundred and thirty years ago the English botanist Brown observed that minute particles in certain plant fluids were perpetually quivering, moving hither and thither in directions quite independent of one another, unlike the motes in a sunbeam, which go in drifts, and indicate general currents in the air. Gradually, by repeated experiment, towards the close of the nineteenth century the various superficial explanations of the Brownian movement—that it was due to the shaking of the building, to currents caused by the illuminating light, and so on—were conclusively disproved. Finally, Jean Perrin recognized that the motion was due to molecular bombardment not quite balanced in all directions: it was, he said, *éternel et spontané*, everlasting and spontaneous. He then undertook systematic measurements, regarding the grains as enormous molecules jostled by the ordinary molecules of the liquid. From precise microscopic observation, performed on a very small drop of water discoloured with the paint gamboge, which breaks up into minute spheres of horny substance when rubbed in the liquid, he was able to calculate not only that the movement of the particles was perfectly explained by the heat movement of the water molecules, but also to deduce the number of molecules in a given weight of any substance. The number of molecules in an ounce of water is something under a million million million million, which means that if every man, woman, and child in the world were turned to counting them, and counted fast, say five a second, day and night, it would take about four million years to complete the job. This figure has been confirmed by a variety of experiments based on quite different principles.

By application of the gas laws to the microscopically visible particles Perrin was also able to show that such particles, suspended in a very thin layer of water, provided a model of the atmosphere, the number of particles decreasing with the height within this minute range. It is, perhaps, one of the most astonishing consequences of precise thought and experiment in modern physics that observations made on a drop of dirty water, requiring only a microscope adapted for accurate measurement, should have led to a very good estimate of the number of molecules in a given weight of substance and of their individual energy of motion.

It appears, then, that in a liquid microscopic particles may be thrown upwards by the molecular agitation. If an intelligent microbe were building a house he could wait to have his bricks thrown up to him: the energy required would be taken from the molecular energy of the liquid, which is heat, so that by the time the microbe's house was built the liquid would be a little cooler, to compensate for the energy required to raise the bricks. The microbe would have apparently violated the second law of thermodynamics, but this does not distress us, as the second law only governs the behaviour of matter in bulk, and would not apply if we could employ creatures small enough to make a discriminating interference with the molecular mechanism —which we cannot. The bigger the particles the less probable a perceptible movement due to molecular agitation: with a visible brick we might have to watch for millions of centuries to see it jump, but we cannot say that the jump is absolutely impossible.

This statistical way of regarding physical problems, this conception that what we see is just an average effect, and that we must be very careful before we attribute to individual molecules properties and laws which we have discovered from observing matter in bulk, is assuming a very large part in modern physics. The conservation of energy itself is a law which entirely suits all our ordinary observation, but at one time it was even suggested that it might not apply to processes happening within the atom. This illustrates the caution, the scepticism—one might almost say the timidity—which has found a place in scientific thought as a result of the many baffling phenomena which have come to our knowledge in recent years. At one time universal validity was attributed to any law which had a success with a wide range of experiments: to-day the utmost care is taken in distinguishing between facts of observation and speculative processes introduced to explain them, and, as far as possible, the theories deal only with the facts. At the beginning of the century there was even a movement against the atomic theory, as at that time there was no convincing *direct* evidence for the existence of atoms and atomic agitation; but Perrin's experiments on the Brownian motion, made round about 1910, and, since then, a great range of other fundamental experiments, have established the objective existence of atoms as far as the objective existence of anything can be established.

What we have said so far about heat and atomic motion applies very well under ordinary conditions, by which we mean in particular at ordinary temperatures, such as can be found in factory, foundry, and workshop. At very high or at very low temperatures, however, the ordinary rules of the physics of fifty years ago do not hold. One of the most exciting fields of physical research at the present time is that concerned with the production of extremely low temperatures and with the properties of matter at such temperatures. Round about the beginning of the century the Dutch physicist Kamerlingh Onnes set up at Leyden a cryogenic laboratory, that is, a laboratory devoted entirely to very low temperatures, the first of its kind. There, over the years, he showed how to get within less than 1° C of the absolute zero of temperature.

This absolute zero is a very important conception: it represents a temperature below which we cannot conceivably go. To discuss it in any way fully would mean an examination of the question of how we define a scale of temperature, which is by no means as simple as it may seem, especially at low temperatures. It is, for example, no help to say that equal expansions of the mercury in the thermometer represent equal rises of temperature, because if we took another substance in our thermometer we should get a slightly different scale, and there seems no point in giving mercury the preference. Anyhow, mercury freezes at 39° C below zero, and so cannot be used to give a scale at such low temperatures.

Theoretical reasons indicate that an ideal gas, without the slight traces of memory of a liquid state which actual gases show in their behaviour, would be the right substance to use to measure temperature. There is no such thing, of course, as an ideal gas, but we can calculate how far the behaviour of any real gas deviates from that ideal, just as we can measure how far any real solid deviates from the ideal of perfect rigidity. It so happens that the temperature scale of a perfect gas agrees pretty well with the mercury thermometer, with equal divisions, over the range of temperature for which mercury can be used. Now, this ideal gas at a certain degree of cold would shrink to no volume at all, and that degree of cold represents the absolute zero, below which we cannot go by any conceivable process. We cannot think of any substance as having less than no volume. The absolute zero indicated by the ideal gas thermometer is 273° C below the temperature of melting ice: the boiling-point of water is, of course, 100° C above the temperature of melting ice.

At the exceedingly low temperatures reached in the laboratory of Kamerlingh Onnes every known gas becomes first liquid and then solid. The last gas to stand out was helium, and that was first liquefied in 1908 and then solidified in 1927 at a temperature only about one degree above the absolute zero. We can find out something about the energy of the molecules of a substance by measuring the specific heat, which is the heat which must be added to raise the temperature of the substance by 1° C. An astonishing result is that at these low temperatures the specific heat is nearly nothing; for instance, it requires only a twenty-fifth as much heat to raise the temperature of a pound of aluminium from 30° above absolute zero to 31° above absolute zero as it does to raise it by one degree at ordinary temperatures, and at still lower temperatures the specific heat is much smaller. These very low specific heats at low temperatures have very great importance for modern physical theory, as considered later in Chapter VII.

Another surprising and significant effect is that at these exceedingly low temperatures many metals lose practically all resistance to the flow of electricity or, as we say, they become super-conductors of electricity. The term 'super'—often used by cinema magnates without any very striking justification—really is justified in this case, as may be judged by the fact that a thousand miles of lead wire at 5° above absolute zero offers no more resistance to the passage of electricity than one inch of copper wire of the same diameter at ordinary temperatures. Investigation of this effect is one of the most fascinating fields of modern physical research. All the properties of matter at these exceedingly low temperatures are, in fact, remarkable and full of interest.

Thirty years ago, as has been said, Kamerlingh Onnes got within 1° of absolute zero. It might seem on the face of it that 1° on the absolute scale (often written 1° K, for Kelvin[6]) is so near to absolute zero that it would not be worth any great effort to push the temperature lower. Actually at these very low temperatures it is more in accordance with the scientific significance of absolute temperature to think of the ratio of two temperatures than of their difference. Thus when we go from 1° K to 0.5° K it represents the scientific achievement better to say that we have halved the temperature than to say that we have lowered it by half a degree, and similarly when we go to 0.25° K we have halved the temperature again. This way of thinking helps us to understand how it is that the absolute zero is unattainable, although we can come very near to it, for even if we succeed in halving the temperature a number of times we still have not reduced it to nothing at all. It also makes understandable what Sir Francis Simon, a great leader in low temperature research, means when he speaks of certain methods as enabling us to cover an enormous temperature range below 1°. From 0° to 1° K *is* an enormous range—from 300° to 301° K (27° C to 28° C) is not.

One of the most extraordinary examples of the way in which everything becomes queer in the neighbourhood of the absolute zero is the behaviour of liquid helium. Helium is a gas with a romantic history. A particular bright line discovered in the spectrum of the sun's light in 1868 could not be identified as belonging to any element which had been tested on earth and it was consequently put down to an unknown element, to which the name helium, the sun element (from Greek *helios,* the sun), was given. In 1895, nearly thirty years after its christening, William Ramsay discovered a new gas on earth which gave the same bright

[6] William Thomson, to whom many of the early advances in the matter of the temperature scale are due. He was much concerned with the early development of transatlantic telegraphy and this, no doubt, was one of the considerations that led to his being made Lord Kelvin in 1892.

spectral line, and so was identified as the sun element, helium. It does not combine chemically with any other element and is the lightest of the family of noble, or rare, or inert gases, for they go by all three names. We shall see later that it is a most important element in modern physics: in fact everything about it is remarkable.

At ordinary atmospheric pressure helium, once liquefied, remains liquid to the lowest temperature that can be reached, say a hundredth of a degree above absolute zero. To cause it to go solid a pressure of 25 atmospheres or more, as well as extreme cold, is necessary. Recent research has shown that there are two forms of liquid helium. That known as helium II is a completely crazy substance. In certain circumstances it conducts heat ten thousand times as well as copper, whereas ordinary liquids are extremely bad conductors compared to metals. When confined in a tube in a certain way it rushes upward of its own accord to form a fountain. It creeps up the side of vessels in which it is filled and runs down the outside. Sound has two different velocities in it. Every now and then a theoretical paper is written to explain this unexpected behaviour, but so far it cannot be said that there is any general agreement among the theories. These queer properties have been mentioned here to show the kind of fascinating problems that the study of very low temperatures has revealed.

At the other end of the scale we might suppose that as the temperature is raised higher and higher the molecules simply rush about more and more vigorously, and the older point of view was that this was the case: the properties of gases at higher temperatures were taken to be just a natural extension of those at the lower temperatures. We know now, however, that it is incorrect to treat the molecules as little balls whose speed of motion can be indefinitely increased by raising the temperature. When the temperature rises above a certain point the molecules begin to fall to pieces, to dissociate into the atoms which compose them, just as a cluster of balls glued together would break up into the individual balls if it were vigorously struck. If the temperature is raised still more the atoms themselves begin to come to pieces, losing their electrons group by group, until nothing is left but atomic nuclei and unconnected electrons.[7] Temperatures which remove a few of the electrons from atoms can be attained on earth, but the temperatures at which all the electrons are stripped from the nucleus as the seed is knocked from a dandelion head, leaving nothing but the central knob, can only be attained in hot stars. This conception of atoms which are broken up when the impacts of atom on atom are sufficiently vigorous has proved of the greatest importance in astronomy, for in the interior of stars the prevailing temperature seems to be in the neighbourhood of 40,000,000° C, as against the highest terrestrial temperature of a few thousand degrees. Once more the application of laws obtained for one set of circumstances to quite different circumstances would arouse grave difficulties. We are led, whether we want to or no, into the realms of atomic structure. The older laws of heat, which took no account of anything but the behaviour of matter in bulk under what we may call engineering conditions, do not suffice to explain either the problems of heat radiation at very high temperatures or of heat vibration at very low temperatures. We must postpone what we have to say on these subjects until we have had a word about the modern ideas.

[7] The modern theory of the structure of the atom is discussed in Chapter VIII.

CHAPTER III

## About Sound and Vibrations

THERE is no branch of physics in which we are not brought sooner or later—generally sooner—to the study of vibrations, the study of waves, the study of processes which repeat themselves over and over again as does, to take the simplest case, the motion of a pendulum. The physicist calls such processes periodic phenomena. All of them have certain fundamental characteristics, of which the most obvious is the time period—that is, the length of time in which one cycle takes place. A pendulum takes so long to execute one complete beat, there and back, and then starts over again; a spinning flywheel takes so long to carry out exactly one revolution, and then, every part of it being in exactly the same position as before, the next revolution begins; a violin string sounding a given note requires just such a fraction of a second to complete a full swing backwards and for- wards; a wireless wave, which is an oscillation of electric and magnetic force, repeats itself at a given place with just such an interval between the exact repetitions.

All vibrations, oscillations, and waves, then, possess a characteristic periodic time. Another way of stating the same thing is that they possess a characteristic frequency, the frequency being the number of complete vibrations in unit time—say one second. Of course, if we know the pe- riodic time, then we can find the frequency, and *vice versa* —if the periodic time is 1/10 of a second, the frequency is

10 vibrations a second. Which we use is a matter of choice. In the case of very rapid alternations, like those of a sound vibration, and still more so those of a wireless wave, it is more usual to state the frequency, since it is more convenient to speak of, say, a frequency of 256 vibrations a second than of a periodic time of 1/256 of a second.

The study of sound is really the study of vibrations of material bodies. Light vibrations come to us from the sun across space empty of matter, so that, whatever light may be, it is not a swinging of material substance, in the ordinary sense. Sound, however, requires a solid, or a liquid, or a gas if it is to travel; the man in the moon could see any light signal we might make, but could not hear any shout, however loud. Solids convey sound very well, a fact familiar to the heroes of old adventure stories, who put their ears to the ground to hear the hoof-beats of approaching horsemen. A very effective experiment on the propagation of sound through a wooden rod some thirty feet long was shown by John Tyndall. In the basement below the lecture-room, separated from it by two floors, was a man playing a piano. A wooden rod resting on the sound board of the piano passed through holes in the floors into the lecture-room. When a wooden tray was placed on the top of the rod the playing of the piano became distinctly audible in the room. The sound vibrations, passing along the rod, threw the tray into vibration, and the vibrations of the tray communicated themselves to the air. The experiment could be made more startling by placing a violin or a harp at the upper end of the rod, to act as the sounding board.

Turning to liquids, bathers can easily verify that water conveys sound very well, for the beat of a ship's screw can be detected when the ship is still far off by putting the head under water. Elaborate methods were worked out during the First World War for detecting the positions of submarines by the sound of the engine conveyed through the water to special microphones. More recent methods for locating submarines involve beams of sound sent out through the water: they will be briefly described later.

As for gases, sound ordinarily reaches our ears through the air, and there are many simple experiments showing that it passes equally well through other gases. The old experiment of a bell, driven electrically or by clockwork, and carefully suspended by thin rubber threads in a jar from which air is then pumped out, shows, on the other hand, that sound cannot pass through a vacuum, for as the pumping proceeds the ringing becomes fainter and fainter, until finally nothing can be heard. Of course, if the bell is placed on the plate at the bottom of the jar, instead of being hung by thin threads which conduct the sound badly, the sound passes through the stand to the table, and communicates itself to the air in the room.

The study of sound includes three separate divisions: the behaviour of the sounding body, which is a study of vibrations; the passage of the sound from the source to the place where it is detected, which is a study of waves; and the way in which the ear acts, which is included in the general question of the behaviour of sense organs. The perception of sound by the ear involves, of course, physical considerations, but it is generally considered a matter of physiology, and will accordingly be put on one side here. As regards the origin of sound, we are lucky in being able to observe directly the way in which the vibrations take place, which we cannot do in the case of light. It is true that the frequency of the vibration of a body giving out a musical note is so high—e.g. 256 per second in the case of the middle C —that the movement cannot be followed by the unaided eye. A violin string or a tuning-fork when sounding appears merely blurred, but there are plenty of ways in which the modes of vibration can be analysed.

The pitch of the note is fixed by the number of vibrations a second and nothing else: thus, whether the middle C is sounded on an organ-pipe or a violin or a piano, there are 256 complete cycles of vibration of the air column enclosed in the pipe, or of the string of the violin or piano respectively, in a second. In this way it is possible to give the number of wing-beats a second of a bee, or wasp, or a gnat, simply by tuning a string to the note of the humming of the insect, and afterwards finding out the number of vibrations per second in the note of the string, either by calculation from the dimension of the string and the tightness with which it is stretched, or by some other method. Of course, if the listener has an ear accurate enough for him to name precisely the position of the note of the insect in the musical scale, the problem is solved at once, since the frequency of each note is known: thus if a bee is humming the G below the middle C its wings must be beating 192 times a second, while a common fly sounding the F above the middle C must be making about 340 wing-movements a second.

The loudness of the note is given by the vigour of the vibration, the greater the full swing of the string, or other sounding body, the more intense being the sound. Pitch and loudness are two characteristics of a musical note: the third characteristic of the note, the timbre or tone-colour, as the Germans call it, is given by the character of the vibration. The character in question is the peculiarity by which, for instance, the note of a trumpet differs from the note of a piano, although both may be sounding the middle C with equal loudness. If the sounding body move out at a uniform speed to its extreme position, and then returns at uniform speed, passing to the other extreme position, we have a different character of note from what is produced if the body moves like a pendulum, fastest through what is the position of rest and slower and slower as the extreme of the swing is approached. The peculiarities of the vibrations of the body are reproduced in the form of the sound wave which it generates, for any disturbance which the string, say, produces in the air just in contact with it travels out with the speed of sound as fast as it is produced. The same thing is true of light or wireless waves: every peculiarity in the form of the wave itself must correspond to a peculiarity in the vibration which gives rise to the wave, but with light it is not possible to examine the vibrating body, the atom itself, and we have to draw our deductions of its behaviour from the form of the waves which it sends out.

It is often a matter of surprise to the plain man that the movement of a single small diaphragm, such as the mica disc in the sound-box of a good gramophone, can reproduce, say, the complicated sound of an orchestra with strings, wood-wind, brass and drums, perhaps all playing at the same instant. The sound of a single instrument is complicated enough, for, besides the fundamental vibration, which gives the pitch of the note, we have present in the case of strings, to take a simple example, several harmonic overtones—the octave, the fifth above the octave, the double octave, and so on—which a trained ear can detect. As the frequencies of these overtones are two, three, four, and so on times the frequency of the fundamental note, the time period of the fundamental just includes a whole number of vibrations of the overtones: a complete cycle is still included within the time period of the note itself, and the only effect of the overtones is to alter the form of the vibration—to affect, for example, the instant within the time period when the vibration is half-way to its greatest value. The ear possesses the remarkable power of analysing the complicated wave form into its simplest parts, and picking out the various harmonics which are sounding simultaneously. It is worth noting, perhaps, that the eye has not this power of analysis: a white light, for instance, can be produced by mixing all colours in suitable proportions, by mixing only two colours in suitable proportions, or by mixing three or more colours. The final white can be made to appear the same to the eye no matter how it is produced, and in a similar way the eye cannot, without instrumental aid, detect what pure colours have been combined to produce any particular mixed colour, or chord of colour, as we may call it to strengthen our analogy.

What is produced by a plucked string is, then, a wave of characteristic shape. In the same way many instruments sounding simultaneously produce a wave of still more complicated shape, but, naturally, however many different sounds are going on at once, the result at a given place in the air can, at a given instant, be only one movement. Any given little bit of air cannot be in more than one place at once: what that place is at a given instant is determined by the combined effect of all the sounds passing the given spot. To take an illustration, no matter how complicated the transactions in a shop, how many purchases and sales, if the total balance be struck at any moment there can only be one definite sum as a result, although it needs a careful analysis to see how that is reached. The result of the orchestral air-pushing is, then, that a wave of very complicated nature is launched on the air, the air particles striking a balance of the various pushes and pulls which they experience at any moment. This complicated wave is then analysed by the ear, the more trained the listener (other things being equal), the more complete being the analysis.

When a record is made, the diaphragm, which governs the needle used to cut the indentations, is moved by the complicated wave so as to record the resultant motion produced by all the instruments. Similarly, when the record is played, the indentations move the diaphragm of the sound-box in just the same complicated way, with little jerks, ripples, and peaks of motion imposed on the fundamental wave, and a wave is launched of exactly the same form as that produced originally by the orchestra. Naturally, therefore, the result on the ear is the same.

It is well, perhaps, to devote some little consideration to the nature of a wave. The breaking wave on the beach which is often conjured up by the phrase, is, unfortunately, an exceedingly bad example of what is meant by a wave in physics: the ripple on a pond produced by dropping in a stone, or the long, smooth rollers out at sea are exceedingly good examples. The characteristic is that, at any given spot, a periodic, or pendulum-like, motion is taking place, and no general forward motion of the medium—air, water, or what not—through which the wave is moving forward. Little boys who, when their boats are becalmed on the pond, throw stones or bricks beyond them so that the waves produced shall bear the boat back, have experience of this (which, however, does not seem to profit them). As the wave reaches the toy boat the main effect is to raise it up and down: it does not move it forward perceptibly. A cork on the pond bobs up and down as the ripple passes it, but does not move along with the ripple crest. What is propagated is the form of the wave.

A good illustration of what we mean by a wave can be seen when a long line of soldiers dresses by the right. If the man on the extreme right were to make a small movement forward every man, dressing by his neighbour, would successively make a small movement forward, and a ripple would run along the line from right to left, but no individual man would be moving from right to left. If the right-hand man were to make a small movement forward and backward at quite regular intervals, say every two seconds, we should have a perfect example of a wave of frequency thirty a minute. Every man in his place would likewise be making a movement forward and backward thirty times a minute, but each man would be a little behind his right-hand man in this movement. If the men were halted sharply the line would be wavy, the successive distance between men who were in the same position and at the same stage of their movement being called the wave-length. While the wavy movement was in progress, at one moment one man would be at the extreme forward position, at the next moment it would be his left-hand man. The position of the particular man in the forward position would run along the line, corresponding to the advance of the crest of a wave.

In the case of this line of men dressing, the movement of any individual man is at right-angles to the direction in which the wave is travelling, namely at right-angles to the line. Such a wave is called a transverse wave. A wireless wave or a light wave is this kind of wave: there is an electric force and an accompanying magnetic force, at right-angles to the direction in which the wave is travelling, and the strength of these forces is fluctuating periodically all the time the wave is passing. If we could place at a given point an inconceivably small electric charge and watch it, and a wireless wave[1] were passing through our house from the north, then the electric charge would bob up and down vertically under the influence of the periodic electric force, like the cork on the water ripple. At the same time an inconceivably minute magnetic pole would move backwards and forwards horizontally from east to west and back again.

A sound wave in air, however, is not a transverse wave. Imagine again our line of men, but this time in Indian file, and let each one place his hands on the shoulders of the man in front of him. If now someone gives the rear man a violent push he will move forward in the direction of the line, and push the man in front of him. A jostle, as it were —that is, a place where the men are nearer to one another than they ought to be—will run along the line. If, now, a strong man takes the rear man and pulls him back he will pull the man in front of him, and so on, and a pull will run along the line. If the rear man is rocked backwards and forwards, jostles succeeded by pulls, regions where the men are more closely crowded than normal followed by regions where they are less closely crowded than normal, will be continually propagated along the line. Such is a sound wave in air, regions of pressure and rarification moving forward with what we call the velocity of sound. The actual movement of a particle of air is backwards and forwards *along*, and not across, the line on which the wave is travelling: we speak of a longitudinal wave.

In the interior of a liquid or a gas, we can have only longitudinal waves, for, if we pluck a particle aside, there is no force to pull it back and make it swing, as there is if we pluck a string aside. We can, however, get transverse waves in a string, as can be seen by shaking one end of a long cord backwards and forwards in a cross-wise direction, and we can have still other forms of waves in a long bar, such as waves of twist. In earthquakes, which are, of course, disturbances running through the solid crust of the

[1] Actually what we say assumes the wave to be polarized in the horizontal plane, but this is a simplification that does not affect the general picture.

earth, complicated forms of waves, with different velocities, have to be taken into account by seismologists, as earthquake men are called.

The form of the sound wave in air is given by the sheet of instructions, as it were, which govern the movement backwards and forwards of the individual little speck of air. If it swings gracefully to and fro like a pendulum we have the simplest possible wave, a pure musical note, but it may move jerkily with little sweeps of advance, or even with little advances and retreats on top of the main movement, as if each man in our Indian file had a fit of shivers as well as a gentle sway backwards and forwards. In that case we have a complicated aural sensation.

If in a wave there is no general movement forward of any particle from the spot about which it swings, nevertheless the *state of motion* does move forward in the direction of the wave. As long as the rearmost particle is shaken, every other particle vibrates; if the rearmost particle is stopped, then, as soon as the wave from its last movement has passed a given spot, that particle at that spot is still. This means that energy is carried forward along the wave, which is, in any case, pretty clear. If by dabbling my hand up and down in the water I can make a cork twenty yards off move up and down, then clearly I am supplying it with energy which travels out with the ripple; the water under my hand does not travel out, but the state of motion does. In all waves, then, there is an actual stream of energy in the direction in which the wave is travelling.

The changes in pressure and the movement backwards and forwards of the air in a sound wave are ordinarily very small. A sound is distinctly audible even when the greatest changes of pressure in the wave are only a few hundred-millionths of the atmospheric pressure, and the greatest swing of the particles is a few hundred-millionths of an inch. Correspondingly the energy of an ordinary sound wave is minute. But if a sound wave be sent through a material which opposes a strong elastic resistance to compression, like an ordinary liquid, and if, by suitable means, the to-

and-fro movement be made considerable, a very great amount of energy can be put into the wave, and travels along with it with very little loss.

Following these principles, an actual system of transmitting energy by sending what are virtually sound waves along liquids enclosed in pipes was devised by Constantinescu. At the sending end, a little piston which, in the case of a particular 10 horse-power generator, was about an inch and a half in diameter, with a one-inch stroke, was given a rapid to-and-fro motion by the engine whose power was to be transmitted. In the case cited the greatest pressure reached during the stroke was 1500 pounds per square inch. The energy in a sound wave increases very rapidly if the frequency is increased, other things being equal, because the speed with which the particles of matter are swinging is proportional to the frequency, and the energy depends upon the square of the speed. The frequency of the stroke was therefore made as high as conveniently possible—40 strokes per second with the 10 horse-power set in question, which gives a note E two octaves below the middle C. The waves generated by the high-speed piston travelled along a pipeline, 240 feet long in our example, and at the other end drove an engine of any desired kind, by pushing and pulling a plunger similar to that which started the wave, with an energy equal to that put into the waves at the generating end, except for small frictional losses.

It must be clearly understood that, when the piston moves in at the starting end, the whole body of the liquid does not move and push the piston at the far end; rather, a region of high compression is created at the piston, which runs through the liquid in the pipe and pushes the piston at the far end, and, similarly, when the generating piston is withdrawn, a region of low pressure (or stretch of the liquid, or tension, whichever term we choose to employ) is created which runs through the liquid and pulls the far piston when it reaches it. There is a true wave motion running through the liquid and delivering energy.

The Constantinescu method has been applied in mining

operations. It may be noted that it first came into prominence during the First World War, when the inventor utilized it to synchronize machine-gun fire with the revolutions of an aeroplane engine, so that the aviator could fire through his propeller without hitting the blades. By connecting to the gun a tube of liquid carrying waves generated by the engine the firing could be so timed that the bullet always passed at the right moment. It seems a long time ago to the days when aeroplanes were so built that it was an advantage, if not absolutely necessary, to fire through the propeller.

Transmission by wave motion is commoner than one is apt to think. For instance, if a long steel rod is put against a rivet and struck sharply with a hammer at the far end, a wave of compression runs along it which delivers the blow to the rivet. This principle has been used to measure the energy of detonation of an explosion, using a small charge of explosive to deliver the blow, and making the wave throw off a small piece of metal at the far end, the speed of which can be measured in a simple way. Even with a hammer and a steel chisel the blow is not transmitted instantaneously from the hammer to the object under the chisel edge: the wave of compression takes about a twenty-thousandth of a second to pass from one end of the chisel to the other.

A sound wave, in addition to the rapidly alternating push and pull which it creates, exerts a small general forward pressure whenever it meets a surface: if it is absorbed by the surface the pressure is only half as great as if it is reflected, completely turned back on itself, by the surface. As a matter of fact, this pressure is a property not only of sound waves, but of all kinds of waves, although wherever the energy of the wave, of whatsoever nature it be, is small the pressure is very small. It was at one time believed that the little radiometers often seen in jewellers' and opticians' windows, little systems of delicately pivoted vanes enclosed in an exhausted bulb, which rotate rapidly when sunlight falls on them, showed the pressure of light, but actually in this case the effect is a heat effect associated with the traces of gas left in the bulb. The pressure of light can, however, be shown experimentally by using very delicate suspension of the vanes instead of the comparatively coarse pivot, and by securing very high exhaustion of the bulb, but it demands great skill to measure this pressure accurately. The pressure of sound can also be shown with a delicately suspended disc, but the sound has to be loud to produce measurable effects. Such a disc, called a Rayleigh disc after its inventor, can be used to measure the intensity of sounds.

We have frequently cited light in speaking of sound, since they both have certain common properties due to the fact that they are both wave motions, although sound waves in air are longitudinal, while light waves are transverse. Similarly, sources of sound, which are mechanical vibrating systems, have close analogies in other branches of physics, especially in the oscillating electrical systems which wireless telephony, broadcasting, and television have made familiar. In systems of condensers, capacities, resistances, and thermionic valves of all kinds charges of electricity oscillate with certain frequencies, certain amplitudes, and a certain displacement pattern, and give rise to electromagnetic waves which travel out through space, just as in a gramophone sound-box a system of masses, springs, and yielding substances, such as rubber rings, oscillate and start sound waves on their journey through the air. The connection between the electrical and the mechanical sources of sound, the wireless oscillator and the gramophone sound-box, is much closer than might be expected: inductance, capacity, current, and charge in the one case, for instance, correspond exactly to mass, yieldingness[2] of spring, speed of moving part, and distance through which moving part has moved in the other case. Similar formulae can, with such-like correspondences, be applied to either case.

This is not only a very good example of the kind of generality which we often meet in mathematical physics, but it is also a case that has had considerable practical importance. The great improvement that has taken place in the

[2] Called 'compliance' by the workers in this field. It is the reciprocal of stiffness.

gramophone since 1925 has been due not only to the application of wireless apparatus in the recording of music, but also to the application of the knowledge, acquired in the development of radio and television, of the behaviour of oscillatory electricity in complicated circuits to the problem of oscillating mica or metal diaphragms exposed to all the modifying influences which exist in the gramophone. The re-designing of sound-box and horn was carried out with the aid of mathematical analogies drawn from electrical cases, which have been so thoroughly studied. There has, in fact, arisen a race of men who think of the electrical quantities as fundamental and familiar, and explain the mechanical quantities, which seem more familiar to most of the older men, in terms of them. In the earlier days of alternating current development it was customary to build mechanical models with masses and cog-wheels to explain electrical self-induction: to this new race, however, self-induction is a fundamental thing that needs no explanation, and they would make use of what they know of it to help them to understand the behaviour of the simple mechanical model.

There are many other directions in which the developments of wireless technique, in particular the effective design of oscillating circuits of all kinds, have led to great developments in the study of sound. One of the most important is the study of mechanical vibrations of very high frequency, to which the name ultrasonics has been given, to indicate that the frequency is far beyond frequencies that can be heard. The ear can detect frequencies of some 20,000 a second, or perhaps a little higher in exceptional cases. As a general rule the ability to hear very high notes decreases with age: for instance, the very shrill squeak of a bat is easily heard by most youngsters, but is too high for many older people.

The difficulty of producing very high rates of mechanical vibrations is to find an arrangement that has a natural high frequency of vibrations. The frequency of a vibrating system depends upon the ratio of the restoring force, tending to pull back to its original position any part of the body that has been displaced, to the mass moved. Thus, with the tuning-fork, the shorter and stouter, that is, the stiffer its prongs, the higher the note. With the 'cello, to lower the frequencies of the strings designed for the low notes they are loaded by being wound with fine wire, which increases the mass, but leaves the stiffness the same. A very stiff vibrator is provided by a metal cylinder struck in the lengthwise direction so that it shrinks momentarily and then recovers and overshoots, continuing this alternating process and so vibrating with a concertina motion. It takes a very large force to produce a very small compression, or, putting it the other way, a small compression, or equally a small extension, leads to a very large restoring force. It is easy to verify this by striking a metal rod sharply with a hammer, as if trying to drive it on: a high note results. The shorter the rod, the higher the note. In fact the frequency of a steel rod 100 inches long, vibrating lengthwise, would be about 1000 a second, two octaves above the middle C; of a rod 10 inches long it would be 10,000 a second, very high, but still audible to most people; of a rod only 1 inch long it would be 100,000 a second, far into the ultrasonic field.

The problem is, then, to find a method of maintaining a short cylinder in steady and continuous lengthwise—or concertina-wise—vibration. Advantage can be taken of a curious fact discovered in 1880 by Pierre Curie—who was later to become world-famous for his leading part in the discovery of radium—and his brother Jacques. Pierre, by the way, was twenty-one at the time, a bright boy. The Curies found that if a slab of crystalline quartz, cut in a certain direction with respect to the natural crystal axes, was compressed, electrical charges, of opposite sign, developed on the opposite faces. They further discovered the reverse effect, which follows theoretically from the original discovery, namely that an electric field, created by applying a difference of voltage to metal layers in contact with the faces of the crystal, produces an expansion or a shrinking of the solid, according as the field is in one direction or other. This effect is very small: for instance, a potential difference of 10,000 volts gives a change of thickness of the crystal of about a millionth of an inch. This phenomenon is called piezo-electricity, that is, pressure-electricity.

It was not until 1917, thirty-seven years after the original discovery, that Langevin succeeded in exciting and main-taining oscillations in a quartz slab by putting it between metal plates and inserting it, as a condenser, in an electric circuit tuned to the frequency of vibration of the quartz. The reason for the long delay is that electric circuits of this kind were not practicable before the development of the thermionic valve, which was rapidly coming into use at the time in question. The alternating field across the quartz pro-duces alternate increases and decreases in the thickness of the slabs, and if the frequency is exactly right, exactly that which the length, stiffness, and density of the solid slice en-tail, the slab oscillates vigorously, the movement building up until the energy supplied is equal to the energy dissipated. This is a good example of resonance, the name given to the particular response of a vibrating system which has a fre-quency of its own to a force of the same frequency, or, to a lesser degree, to a force of nearly the same frequency. Resonance is a phenomenon that runs through the whole of the field of electrical and mechanical vibrations of all kinds. The sharpness of the response depends upon the frictional forces, of one kind or another, tending to stop the system vibrating. To set an apple tree into vibration by periodic pushes does not need particularly accurate timing: to set a violin string into vibration by placing a tuning-fork on the bridge needs very accurate adjustment.

The natural frequency of a quartz slab is very high: for a thickness of one inch it is 110,000 vibrations per second and for one-tenth inch it is 1,100,000—figures much the same as for steel. Quartz discs of very small thickness in-deed have been brought into vibration by the electric-circuit method. A case is recorded where the thickness was only two-thousandths of an inch, with a corresponding frequency of about 50 million vibrations per second, but naturally such specimens are very fragile.

Even in the region of a few hundred thousand vibrations a second oscillating quartzes produce extraordinary effects, some of which are ordinary sound properties very much exaggerated. The actual to-and-fro motion of the particles of the liquid or solid through which the waves are travelling is always very small, not more than a few hundred-thousandths of an inch, but, on account of the resistance to compression of the medium and of the rapidity with which the motion is taking place, the energy of the wave is very great compared to ordinary sound waves. The pressure of sound, for instance, which, as has been stated, requires delicate instruments to detect with ordinary sounds, even when very loud, shows itself in many striking ways when ultrasonic waves are in question. If an oscillating quartz plate is put flat on the bottom of a vessel of oil, so that the waves travel upwards, the surface of the liquid may be raised in a mound three inches high by the sound pressure, and a fountain of drops surmounts the mound. The pressure, in a particular case, supported a plate weighing six ounces.

It may be mentioned that there is another way in which instantaneous contraction of a solid can be produced without applying mechanical pressure. A rod of magnetic material, say iron or nickel, changes its length slightly when magnetized, the so-called magneto-striction effect. If, then, such a rod be placed in a coil conveying a rapid alternating current of suitable frequency, it can be brought into vibration. The method has been used and frequencies up to 25,-000 per second have been produced, but for purposes where much higher frequencies are needed the piezo-quartz method dominates the field of ultrasonics.

Ultrasonics, which arose, then, from the coming together of a comparatively old discovery with the comparatively new technique of valve circuits, has found many important applications. The first was due to a quite general wave property which comes up for consideration in the next chapter. We can treat a beam of rays as travelling in parallel straight lines as long as the wave-length is small compared to the hole through which the beam comes, as is the case with light passing through an ordinary aperture an inch or so across, but if the hole limiting the beam is only a wave-length, or a few wave-lengths across, then we have a complicated spreading.

This means that we cannot have a cylindrical, or nearly cylindrical, beam of sound unless the wave-length is small compared to the vibrating plate that starts the sound. Now ordinary sound waves have wave-lengths measured in feet, so that, for anything like a decent beam, we should want a vibrating disc several feet across, moving backwards and forwards as a whole—not tied at the edges. This is not practicable. But with ultrasonic waves a beam can be produced with a reasonable size of oscillating plate. Such a beam in water is an extremely valuable agent for detecting obstacles of all kinds and may be turned to the detection of submarines, icebergs, and reefs; to measuring the depth of the sea and to detecting shoals of fishes; and to directional submarine signalling. Light is useless for these purposes, as it is so heavily absorbed in ordinary sea water, and electromagnetic wireless waves are also too heavily absorbed for submarine use.

The absorption of sound waves in water and in air depends on the frequency, increasing as the frequency rises. The effect in air is easily detected by listening to a distant band: the drums are very clear when the fifes cannot be heard at all. For submarine uses, then, a compromise wave-length, between very long and very short, must be used.

It was Langevin who, using a construction of quartz-crystal slices and steel, first obtained a practicable beam of ultrasonic waves, which was applied for detecting submarines towards the end of the First World War. The wave-length used, short enough to get a well-defined beam and long enough not to be too badly absorbed, was about an inch and a half in water, the diameter of the oscillating plate being a foot or so. Somewhat larger wave-lengths and plates are used nowadays. The principle is to send out at small intervals an ultrasonic beam and, if there is any solid body in the way, to measure its distance by the time between the departure of the sound and the first return of the reflected sound, or echo. This interval is very short, as sound travels in sea water at a speed of just on a mile a second, but by very ingenious methods it may be measured so accurately that distances can be determined to within a few feet, or less if circumstances are favourable.

In peace-time ultrasonic sound-echo apparatus is used for detecting and measuring the distance of icebergs, of which about nine-tenths are under water; for measuring the depth of water under a ship, by reflection from the sea-bottom; for locating wrecks on the sea-bottom and even for locating shoals of fish, which reflect the sound. As the required wavelength is not very short, which means that piezo-quartz oscillators, if used, have to be sandwiched with steel to bring down the frequency, magneto-striction oscillators are widely employed in this type of work.

A somewhat similar application of ultrasonic waves, but one where very high frequencies are required, is for detecting flaws in metal. Waves of very high frequency, a few million cycles per second, are used, which are sent out in pulses, short 'squirts', from an emitter clamped to the specimen, with a detector at its side. The beam of sound is reflected from any serious flaw in the metal, so that, in principle, the method is not unlike depth-sounding in the sea. Piezo-quartz oscillators are widely used but other piezo-electric materials are now being introduced. The method has found wide uses with ingots, castings, forgings, and so on: tool steel, for instance, is easily tested in this way.

Another characteristic of ultrasonic waves is their effect on small particles, of various kinds, floating in gases or liquids. The waves cause smokes, which are small particles of carbon and such-like, floating in air, to coagulate; they turn liquids that do not mix, such as water and oil, into emulsions. They injure microbes and so have been used for sterilizing milk and such-like. The explanation of all these occurrences is complicated, but is, in general, due to the forces set up when a wave passes from one medium to another. Ultrasonic waves have even been used for making fats, waxes, and water form an intimate mixture, and so for manufacturing face-creams. When a discovery, like that of piezo-electricity, has been applied to purposes of war and luxury, in the battleship and in the boudoir, it must be judged, on modern standards, to have justified itself.

The vibrations of quartz crystals are exceptionally stable, being very little influenced by temperature or by age. They have therefore been applied to the measurement of time, and to-day the so-called quartz clock, governed by the vibrating crystal instead of by the pendulum, is used in the great observatories of the world as the most accurate obtainable. In particular, at the Royal Greenwich Observatory, under the direction of Sir Harold Spencer Jones, its superiority has been established. In one type the governing oscillator is a small plate of quartz vibrating at about 100,000 oscillations per second, maintained in vibration by a special type of circuit; in another type a ring of crystal is used which, according to the latest reports, is somewhat superior. Although the frequency of quartz oscillators varies particularly little with temperature, the accuracy required is so high that the crystals are kept in a very carefully controlled constant-temperature enclosure. By ingenious devices the very high frequency is reduced in a perfectly definite ratio so as to govern instruments which enable the time indication to be read without difficulty. The best of such clocks now keep constant time to within one part in ten thousand million, which means about a hundred-thousandth of a second per day, over periods of a month or more. Even over periods of years the clocks are sufficiently stable to enable astronomers to measure yearly fluctuations in the rate of rotation of the earth! The vibrating fragment of quartz keeps a check on the accuracy of the solar system.

# CHAPTER IV
## About Light and Radiation

IF a narrow beam of white light—say sunlight, but the light from an electric lamp will do just as well—from a slit pass through a prism and is properly focussed it becomes a bundle of overlapping narrow beams, fanning out so as to give a long band where it falls on a white screen, in place of the line of light which it forms if no prism be interposed. The band is coloured, the colours ranging from red, through orange, yellow, green, blue and indigo, to violet. The colours blend imperceptibly into one another, so that it is impossible to say exactly where one stops and the next begins, and at either end they shade off so that it is difficult to say just where the band ends. This coloured band is the celebrated spectrum of white light revealed by Newton. Any particular line in the spectrum corresponds to light that has been bent through a certain angle from its original direction.

Now, if we take a certain beam coming out of the prism, say the centre of the yellow, and pass it through a second exactly similar prism, it will be bent aside, or deviated, as the physicist prefers to call it, through exactly the same angle as this particular coloured light was deviated by the first prism: the same holds for a third prism, or any number of prisms. White light, then, contains in itself an infinite variety of different kinds of light, each of which is characterized by being bent through a certain angle by a given prism.

To fix the deviation precisely we have to specify the glass of which the prism is made, because different glasses have different powers of bending light; we must also name the angle of the prism, since a prism with an angle of 60 degrees bends a given kind of light more than a prism of 30 degrees does.

While we can, by virtue of our colour sense, distinguish lights differently bent by their different colours, it is clear that the amount of deviation is a more precise way of indicating the kind of light in question than a mention of the colour is, for lights that are bent by amounts only slightly different appear the same colour to the eye. Further, it is not always easy to state exactly the colour of a given light: a greenish blue, for instance, will be called blue by some, green by others. The deviation of light in its passage from one substance to another—e.g. from air to glass—is called refraction by physicists, and the property of being deviated is called refrangibility, so that we can summarize what has been said so far by saying that white light contains light of all degrees of refrangibility between certain limits, and that a certain refrangibility may be attributed to every simple and pure light—that is, to every light that cannot be further split up by its passage through a prism.

To have discovered all this was one of the great achievements of Sir Isaac Newton. To-day we can go a step further, and say, in more general terms, what it is that really characterizes a monochromatic light, or light of one colour, meaning by colour that exact position in the spectrum given by the refrangibility. We know that light has the properties of a wave motion, and that lights of different colours are distinguished from one another by different frequencies of vibration, the frequency of the extreme visible violet being very nearly twice that of the extreme visible red. This fact is sometimes expressed by saying that the visible spectrum contains one octave of colour, since in sound a note that has twice the frequency of another note is called the octave above it. If, therefore, we want to indicate a particular green light, bent just so much by a given prism, and therefore occupying a precise place in the spectrum, we can specify its frequency, which relieves us of the need of specifying the kind of glass and the angle of the prism. The frequency is the distinguishing number of a pure light, just as it is the distinguishing number of a pure note.

In empty space light of all colours has the same speed, namely 186,326 miles a second, which is more conveniently remembered as almost exactly 300,000 kilometres a second. Now during the time of one complete vibration a wave motion must advance through a distance of exactly one wave-length, so that if we multiply wave-length by frequency (the number of vibrations in a second) we have the distance through which the wave passes in one second, or the velocity. To give the frequency, then, is the same thing as giving the wave-length in empty space (which is very nearly the same as the wave-length in air, since the presence of the air retards the light but little). In solid and liquid substances, say glass or water, however, light travels markedly more slowly than in empty space,[1] and each particular colour travels with a different speed—in fact, it is the difference of speed that leads to the difference of refrangibility. The wave-length of a particular light is therefore different in different substances, but the frequency is everywhere the same.

With visible light the frequency is extremely high, and the wave-length correspondingly small. For a particular yellow light produced when salt is brought into a colourless gas-flame, for instance, the wave-length in air is 0.0000589 centimetre (about 0.0000232 inch), and the frequency 509,100,000,000,000 vibrations per second! Since the velocity of wireless waves is the same as that of light, we can at once calculate the wave-length if we are given the kilocycles, or number of thousand vibrations, a second. An or-

[1] Light has, in ordinary glass, about two-thirds of the speed which it has in empty space, in water about three-quarters.

dinary frequency for wireless waves is 1000 kilocycles, which means a wave-length of 300 metres.[2]

The periodic or wave nature of light is revealed to us by what is termed the interference and the diffraction of light. Let us consider first of all interference, in terms of water ripples. Suppose that we have, hung over the middle of a smooth pond, a spiral spring carrying at its lower end a horizontal rod, bent down vertically at each end so that the extremities, a yard apart, say, nearly touch the water. If the spring is made to vibrate up and down, the two ends of the rod will dip in and out of the water together and cause two series of ripples running out in ever-increasing circles from centres a yard apart. The crests will always leave the centres together in perfect time, since the same movement of the rod gives rise to both series. We ask now what will happen where the two series of ripples overlap. If we choose any point on the pond's surface, the water there will be pushed up and down by each ripple just as if the other were not there, and to find out the movement we must add the movements due to the two separate ripples.

According to the position of the point, it may happen that the movements are exactly in step, when the motion will be just twice as violent as that due to the ripple from one centre alone, or they may be exactly out of step, so that the crest of one ripple system always arrives at the same time as the trough of the other. In this case the two will exactly annul one another, and at this particular point the water will move neither up nor down but will be always at rest. We say that the waves interfere. Clearly, if the point selected is at the same distance from each centre, then the waves will be in step at that point, and therefore we have violent motion all along the line which passes just between the two centres, and is at right-angles to the line joining them. Again, if the point selected is farther from one centre than the other by exactly one wave-length, then the crests will arrive together at this

---

[2] 1000 kilocycles=1,000,000 vibrations a second and 300 metres=0.3 kilometre; 0.3 × 1,000,000=300,000 kilometres a second, the velocity of light.

point, only one system will be a wave behind the other, which makes no difference to what happens, just as, if we see two men running together round a racecourse, we can only say that they have run an equal distance, or that one is a whole lap, or two whole laps, or any number of whole laps behind the other. There will therefore be a series of lines (actually slightly curved lines) on the surface of the pond on which the motion is violent.

Midway between these there will be the points at which one ripple system is exactly half a wave-length behind the other, giving rise to lines along which there is no motion at all. Thus the surface of the pond will be streaked with strips of vigorous wave motion and strips where there is little or no motion. No energy is, of course, destroyed by the interference of the two systems of ripples, but it is removed from some places and heaped up in other places—it is redistributed. If, opposite the two centres, we half immerse a vertical board in the pond, then at some points of the board the water will wash up and down, while at others, in between them, the water will not move. If we pull the board out of the water we shall have a wavy edge to the wet part. Measuring on the board the distance apart of the places where the water was still, and knowing the distance of the board from the centres and the distance apart of the centres, we can easily calculate the wave-length of the ripples.

In the laboratory there is no need to do things on such a large scale, because the two sets of ripples can be produced on the surface of a little pool of mercury by two dipping wires attached rigidly to the prong of a tuning-fork. With suitable illumination the lines along which the disturbances annul one another, in between lines along which they reinforce one another, can be beautifully seen.

We have devoted some little consideration to this ripple case because the interference of waves which it illustrates is of extraordinary importance in the study of vibrations. It is quite easy to obtain interference with sound waves or with 'wireless' waves, but a description of the experiments would lead us a little too far afield.

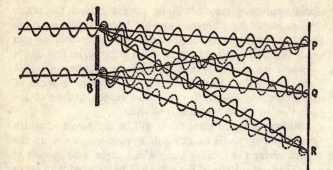

FIG. 1. *To illustrate interference. The light falling on the slits A and B is in step, since it comes from a fine slit far to the left, equidistant from A and B*

Let us now turn to the real object of our study at the moment, the interference of light. The only difficulty is to hit on some way of getting two sources of light in which the vibrations are in step, for that condition is necessary to start with. In the case of the mercury surface we kept the ripples exactly in step at the centres from which they started by governing the dippers with the same vibrating prong. If we put two slits in front of a flame or other source of light, however, the light issuing from them will have been furnished by different parts of the source, and so the two sets of vibrations will be quite unconnected from the start. We shall have no right to expect interference. We can, however, make use of reflection, which gives us an exact duplicate of any luminous point: the light and its image in the mirror supply us with two light sources in which the vibrations of each little part of the one must be exactly in tune with the vibrations of the corresponding part of the other. Or, again, by reflection from two mirrors we can obtain two images of the same light, which two images must be exactly similar to one another in the smallest detail. A third method is to send light to the two slits from a third fine slit, equidistant from the two: each of the operating slits will then be illuminated in exactly the same way. The interference in this case is represented in Fig. 1, where A and B are the slits, producing bright light at P and R, where the waves from A (full lines) and from B (broken lines) are in step, and darkness at Q, where the waves are completely out of step. We have now seen different ways of starting two light waves spreading out in all directions from two different sources at which they are exactly in step. We are also in a position to consider some simple cases of interference of light which confront us in daily life.

A thin film, say a film of oil on water, has two surfaces, and light from any bright spot, say any one particular point of the sky or of a bright cloud, must be reflected from both surfaces into our eye, placed in a suitable position. Of the two beams which enter the eye, one from the top and the other from the bottom surface of the thin sheet of oil, one has gone a little farther than the other, owing to the thickness of the film. For a certain wave-length this extra distance will be just an odd number of half wave-lengths, and therefore any light of this particular wave-length will cancel out at our eye by interference. White light, such as the sunlight we have considered, contains, as we have seen, a great range of wave-lengths: the effect of the film, seen at a certain angle, will be to cancel out one particular kind of light and weaken all in its neighbourhood, and therefore we shall see a coloured film, coloured because, if we remove certain colours from white, the remaining colours no longer make white, but blend to a new tint. For instance, if red is removed from white light we get peacock blue.

Which particular colour cancels out depends upon the thickness of the film, and the angle at which the light comes from it, since the smaller the angle which the arriving light makes with the surface of the film, the longer the difference of path caused by reflection at the two surfaces. All these facts can be verified with ease either with a flat soap film, obtained by dipping a ring of wire into a soap solution, or with a film of oil such as can often be observed lying on water on the road after rain. The oil film will appear differently coloured at different parts owing to its irregular thickness, the changes of colour succeeding one another closely near the edge, where the film tails off quickly into nothing. If the eye be moved, the colour at any particular spot changes.

The flat soap film is particularly interesting, because if it be arranged vertically it will drain away, so as to be very thin above, and thicker below, and a glorious series of horizontal bands of colour will be seen. The colours of the ordinary soap bubble, of thin slivers of mica seen at the edge of a broken piece, of a thin film of air pressed between two really flat pieces of glass, or between a slightly rounded lens surface and a flat glass, of the thin films of fat sometimes found in cooked meat, of the bubbly scum on ponds are all due to interference, and bear silent witness to the wave nature of light.

The colours of thin films are remarkable not only for their beauty and for their scientific importance: they have considerable practical application. If we have one true surface and place another glass surface upon it, any irregularity of the second surface will make itself visible by an irregularity of the colour patches produced by interference of the light reflected from the two glass surfaces. The places where the air film between the two surfaces is irregular in thickness can then be marked, and the surface worked by hand until, when placed on the test surface, or 'optical flat' as it is called, the colour is spread as uniformly as possible. The highest class of optical mirrors and lenses for scientific purposes, such as microscope lenses, are finished in this way, and many delicate measurements can be made by interpreting the message of the light waves about film thicknesses.

If we start with a bright line of light, produced by a slit suitably illuminated, together with its image in a mirror, we have two exactly similar sources of light, and the effect is exactly that illustrated by our example of the ripples on mercury: where the light from the two comes together on a screen we have, alternatively, places where the wave motion is violent and places where it is negligible—in other

words, a series of light and dark bands, the so-called interference fringes. These interference fringes play a most important part in the measurements of the physics laboratory.
Their virtue is that they give a very delicate method of detecting small changes in length. The existence of a bright
band at a particular spot tells us that the difference of the
distances from the two light sources to that spot is exactly
a whole number of wave-lengths, or, fixing for simplicity
the central bright band, that the distance from the centre
of that band to the two sources is exactly equal. If by any
means we slightly change the length of one of the light paths,
even by a distance which is only a fraction of a wave-length
of light, say by a hundred-thousandth of an inch or so, then
the position of the band will clearly shift to a new position
from which the distances *are* equal. If a billiard-cue had a
perfectly flat end, and were stood on this flat end as a base,
a sheet of paper pushed under one side would make the
point of the cue move through quite a large distance, and
in the same way a very small change in one light path makes
the point at which the two paths meet in step swing through
a comparatively large distance, which is detected as a movement of the interference fringes.

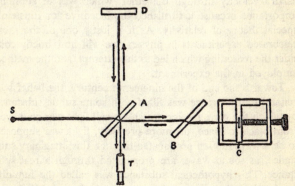

FIG. 2. *The principle of Michelson's interferometer*

How can we alter the length of one of the light paths

without altering the other? The most famous instrument for this purpose we owe to A. A. Michelson, for nearly forty years professor at the Ryerson Physical Laboratory, Chicago. In Michelson's interferometer, as it is called, the light from a slit S (Fig. 2) falls on a plate of glass A placed at 45 degrees to its path; part of the light is reflected off at right-angles to its original path, while part passes on through the glass. The mirror D turns the light which is reflected at A back upon itself, so that part of it passes through A to the observing instrument T: the mirror C, the position of which can be accurately adjusted, sends the light that passes from S through A back upon itself, so that part of it is reflected at A into the instrument T.[3] The two parts of the split beam thus come together again and produce interference fringes seen by T, since only at one point will the two paths be exactly equal. For most of their path, be it noted, the two beams will have been travelling at right-angles to one another. We can alter the length of one path independently by slightly moving the mirror C. Clearly, this instrument provides us with an extraordinarily sensitive way of measuring lengths. It was used in the attempt to measure the earth's velocity through the ether, which was of supreme importance because it furnished the incentive for Einstein's special theory of relativity. As it is justly one of the most celebrated experiments in physics, we will now briefly consider the reasoning which led to this attempt, and the method employed in the experiment.

Towards the end of the nineteenth century, the belief was general that all space was filled with some subtle substance by which the wave motion which we call light was conveyed from place to place, or, more precisely, light was supposed to be a wave motion propagated through this imaginary substance, as sound waves are propagated through a real substance. This hypothetical substance was called the luminiferous ether. Some men of science took the view that you could not have a wave motion without something for it to

[3] The plate B serves a minor but essential purpose.

travel through, but that, as we knew nothing about it except that light travelled through it, the ether was little more than a subject for the verb 'to undulate'. Others considered that it had the physical properties of an elastic solid, and busied themselves trying to work out an elasticity and a density for it. All were agreed on this point: that if the ether had any kind of reality it should be possible to measure the speed with which our earth was passing through it. If we could only do this the ether would give us some absolute standard of rest, and we could speak of a velocity measured with respect to the ether as an absolute velocity, in contrast to velocities with reference to other heavenly bodies which is all that we can measure at present, without being able to say that any particular star is at rest rather than any other heavenly body.

The method proposed for measuring the speed of the earth through the ether depended upon this principle: that if light travelled through a stationary ether, and the earth was likewise moving, though with a much smaller velocity than that of light, through this ether, then a light signal sent out in the direction of the earth's motion and reflected back to its starting-point would take a little longer for its double journey than a signal sent out at right-angles to the direction of the earth's motion and reflected back again, both paths being of equal length. The difference of duration of the two journeys would enable us to calculate the speed of the earth through the ether. It is usual to make this clear by the illustration of a man rowing on a broad river, say a mile wide, flowing steadily in one direction. If he rows down the river from one mile post on the bank to the next, and then back again, clearly the river will help him in one direction and oppose him in the other, but nevertheless he will take longer over this double journey than he will to row across the river and back again along a path at right-angles to the direction of flow.

The reason is clear: he does the journey downstream with a speed obtained by adding the speed of the current to his own rowing speed, and does it quickly, being therefore *helped* by the current during a comparatively *short* time. On the way back he is opposed by the current, and takes a long time over the journey, being *hindered* during a *long* time. Taking an extreme example, supposing his speed on still water is four miles an hour, and that the river current is three miles an hour, he will go downstream at seven miles an hour past the bank, and will do his mile in one seventh, instead of one quarter, of an hour: on his way back, however, he will have a speed of only one mile an hour past the bank, and will take a full hour, instead of one quarter, the total journey occupying an hour and a seventh instead of half an hour on still water. The journey across is also somewhat lengthened by the current, but to a lesser degree; in our particular example it will take about three quarters of an hour instead of the half-hour in still water. If the rower had no other way of measuring the speed of the river, he could, then, clearly do it by timing himself for the two different journeys and comparing the results, knowing only his speed on still water.

In the ether case the velocity of the earth is very small compared to that of light, so that the effect to be expected from the earth's motion would be exceedingly minute—a difference of about one part in a hundred million. This is where the delicacy of the interferometer is essential. Suppose that we can set it up so that one of the two light paths, which lie at right angles to one another, is in the direction of the earth's motion through the ether. Interference fringes will be formed. If we now rotate the whole apparatus through a right-angle the other light path becomes the one in the direction of the earth's motion, and will be the one in which the light is retarded, so that there should be a shift of the fringes if there is any difference of the speed of the light in the two directions. This is the essence of the famous Michelson-Morley experiment, carried out originally in 1887 with the greatest care and skill, and since repeated many times. In one of the repetitions, by Morley and Miller, the lengths of the light paths were, by repeated reflections, made as great as 32 metres each (about 35 yards), which length contains 55 million waves of the yellow light used, so that the change of path to be expected from the earth's motion (one in a hundred million) amounts to over half a wave-length, which is doubled because turning through a right-angle interchanges the paths. There should, therefore, have been a shift of more than a whole interference fringe, and less than a hundredth of this can be measured. When we think that the actual duration of the whole light path of thirty-odd metres is a ten-millionth of a second, that the difference of time on the two paths for which we are looking is a hundred-millionth of this, and that we can measure an effect less than a hundredth of this, the power of the interferometer needs no further emphasis.

The result of the Michelson-Morley type of experiment is negative: no effect of the earth's motion on the speed of light, as measured on the earth, has ever been established. It is true that in 1925 an announcement by Miller that he had obtained a very small effect created a sensation in the world of physics, but he has obtained no further confirmation, and since then two other American experimenters, R. J. Kennedy and K. K. Illingworth, working independently at Pasadena, have made exceedingly careful repetitions of the experiment, with different apparatus, and have obtained no effect whatever. Shortly before his death in 1931 Michelson himself announced that new experiments of his own likewise showed no effect. No motion of the earth through the ether can, therefore, be detected, and this means that there cannot be an ether with the properties of any material body. This conclusion had a fundamental effect on physical theory.

It was to explain this extraordinary effect that Einstein originally devised the theory of relativity, which involves this impossibility of measuring any motion through space by means of light signals. It is fundamental for the theory that no matter with what speed or in what direction the experimenter be moving, he will always find the same result for the velocity of light. The velocity of light is, then, one of the most fundamental quantities in the whole of physics, and has been measured to an extraordinary degree of accuracy. Michelson in the few years before his death made new measurements, and as a result of these announced the velocity of light to be 299,796 kilometres a second, with a possible error of a few kilometres only! Since then the velocity of light, the velocity of radio waves, and the velocity of electromagnetic waves about an inch long has been measured by very different methods of the utmost skill and ingenuity. All these kinds of radiation should have the same velocity, and actually Bergstrand in Sweden with ordinary light found 299,792.7, Aslakson in the U.S.A. with radar waves found 299,794.2, and Essen in England with inch waves found 299,792.5. These figures are quoted to show the precision of modern physical measurements.

To return to the interferometer, a second use to which it has been put is a more practical one—namely its application to the measurement of the standard of length, which arose from the difficulty of making sure that any distance between scratches on a metal bar has the degree of permanence which is required. The length of the bar changes with temperature, but that, of course, can be avoided by making the comparison with the standard always at precisely the same temperature. The length of a metal bar, however, tends to change with age, owing to very slow internal rearrangements of the atoms and, although by great care in the preparation and conditions of storage of the bar these changes can certainly be made exceedingly small, there is still a little uneasiness in the scientific heart at the thought of depending for our standard on any particular bar of metal, rather than on something in Nature that does not change, something that is always at hand whatever happens to any particular piece of stuff.

Originally it was proposed that the earth itself should be taken as our standard, the French metre being defined, when it was legally established in 1800, as one ten-millionth of the distance from pole to equator measured along a meridian, which it very nearly is. This distance, however, cannot be determined accurately enough for our requirements in the matter of standards of length to-day. After much discussion it was proposed to use as the standard of length the wave-length of a certain very pure light given out by cadmium atoms: this element is chosen because the wave-length of certain of its spectral lines is particularly definite, not a mixture of closely neighbouring wave-lengths. The cadmium atom, which is the same at all times and in all parts of the world, is thus made the final appeal.

However, as a wave-length of light is not the kind of thing an engineer can handle, and is not a very convenient thing even for the physicist who wants to measure a length, the problem arises of finding just how many of these wave-lengths there are on whatever bar we have been taking as our standard. We can then check from time to time if the bar is still exactly the same length, and, what is equally important, we can check standard bars in different parts of the world against the standard wave-length provided by the cadmium atom. By the skilful application of Michelson's interferometer the length of the standard metre at Paris was determined in terms of the cadmium wave-length, and we now know that the distance between the scratches on the precious bar contains 1,553,163.5 wave-lengths of red cadmium light (in air at standard temperature and pressure). This result is certainly correct to within one part in a million.[4] Strange as it may appear, therefore, if anyone asks as to where lies our final appeal in matters of length, we point to the light coming from a special kind of electric lamp containing cadmium vapour.

The interferometer is also applied to find out the minute faults of expensive lenses. Here, then, is an instrument which has led to the theory of relativity, helped to establish a standard of length, and aided in the perfecting of photographic lenses. Behind it all lies the wave theory of light, and the magnificent regularity of its behaviour gives us con-

[4] The repetition of the measurement of the metre in terms of cadmium light made, with a different form of apparatus, by MM. Benoît, Fabry, and Perot gave 1,553,164.13, differing from Michelson's value by 1 part in 2,400,000 only!

fidence in our belief that light certainly has the periodic properties of a wave motion, whatever other properties it may have.

A sensational application of the interference properties which light possesses gave us the first measurement of the diameter of a star. Although many stars, the so-called 'giants', are immensely larger than the sun, they are so far off that even with the largest telescope they appear mere points of light, and show no disc whose diameter can be measured. Suppose, now, that we consider light from a single very distant point to fall on two mirrors suitably arranged, and the light from the two mirrors to be brought together by a system of lenses, it is clear from what has been said that interference fringes, alternate light and dark bands, will be produced. The larger the separation of the mirrors, the narrower the fringes. Now consider what happens to the light received, by the same system of mirrors and lenses, from a distant point very near the first distant point. A system of interference fringes will likewise be formed, but a little to one side compared to the first set. If the two distant points are separated by a certain amount the bright parts of the fringes due to one will fall on the dark parts of the fringes due to the other, and no fringes will be visible. The wave-length of light being exceedingly small, a simple calculation shows that, if the mirrors which receive the light from the two points are separated by a distance of some feet, then the angle made by lines drawn from the two points of the light sources to the eye of the observer needs only to be exceedingly small for the fringes to vanish.

For simplicity we have considered the fringes formed by two points: we can apply similar reasoning to a bright disc made up of a number of points. The fringes formed by some of the points will just cancel out those formed by the other points if the angular size of the disc bear a certain relation to the separation of the mirrors and the wave-length of light. Those were the principles on which Michelson set about measuring the size of the giant star Betelgeuse, which is one of the two very bright stars in the familiar constellation of Orion. The two mirrors were fixed on a frame running across the top of the great 100-inch telescope at Mount Wilson, so as to form with the telescope an enormous T, and they were gradually moved apart until the fringes vanished, which occurred when the separation of the mirrors was 10 feet. The wave-length of the effective part of the light being about twenty-three-millionths of an inch, the angular diameter of the star works out to be 0.047 second of arc, which means that from the earth it looks the same size as a bright disc an inch across seen at a distance of 70 miles. This is the interpretation of the message skilfully elicited from the little waves of light, for no possible telescope directly turned on to a disc of that size at that distance would show us that it had any diameter. It is remarkable that the atmosphere is still and clear enough to allow the fringes to be observed: in fact, fear of atmospheric disturbance long prevented any experiment of this kind being made.

It may be added, as an item of information, that, other measurements having shown the distance of Betelgeuse to be about 930 million million miles, we conclude that the diameter of the star is something over 200 million miles, or, in other words, if the centre of the star were placed at the centre of our sun, the orbit of our earth would fall right inside the star, which would, in fact, nearly fill the whole orbit of Mars.

Another aspect of the wave theory now demands our attention. We know that sound waves can turn round corners: a brick wall, for instance, does not cast a sharp sound shadow where it ends, but rather its shielding action is incomplete until we have advanced far into its shelter. The shielding is, however, much sharper for a shrill whistle than for a low note. In the same way the ripples on the surface of a pond will spread somewhat behind any plank or suchlike body placed in the way. If, then, it is a property of waves to bend round the edges of obstacles, how is it that light casts a sharp shadow, and will apparently not turn round corners?

The answer is that the amount of bending at the edge of an obstacle depends upon the wave-length, being greater the greater the wave-length: that with light, owing to the small wave-length, it is very small, that it emphatically does exist, and that light from a narrow source, say a slit, is found *not* to cast a sharp shadow of a straight edge when the matter is carefully investigated, but rather forms a series of very fine alternate dark and light bands parallel to the edge, which are known as diffraction fringes, the bending being technically called diffraction.

If the amount of bending does, in fact, depend upon the wave-length, we shall expect it to be different for different coloured lights, so that when white light grazes an edge there should be a separation of the prismatic colours at the edge of the shadow. This also is found to be true, the red light, which has the longest wave-length, being the most bent, and the violet least. The general fact can be easily verified by looking at the bright filaments of an electric lamp through a fine cambric or nylon handkerchief, when each wire will be seen to be surrounded by a series of coloured fringes. It is upon this phenomenon that systematic measurements of the wave-length of light, especially of spectral lines, are based.

The light from a fine slit is passed through a glass plate ruled, by means of a diamond point, with very close parallel lines. Such a plate is called a diffraction grating, and must be adjusted so that the lines are parallel to the slit. The ruled lines, which are actually minute rough grooves, are comparatively opaque, so that what we really have is a series of very fine clear slits between the lines. The light traversing the plate is turned through an angle which depends upon the wave-length, and also upon the distance between the lines: with the kind of dimensions which are used, namely about 15,000 lines to the inch, the bending is very large. The measurement of the angle of bending is carefully made, and from it the wave-length is deduced.

The theory of diffraction is a little complicated, and what is attempted here is only the roughest indication as to what is in question. The ruling of the gratings is a matter calling for the highest technical skill, and good gratings are very much prized and command high prices. Rowland of Baltimore devoted many years to their production, and in the course of his labours made great improvements in the accurate cutting of screws. So, in physics, one thing leads to another. The preparation of gratings has recently been very much improved by an ingenious, and very simple, method devised by Sir Thomas Merton, which eliminates the very small irregularities that occur even in the most carefully cut screw.

What, then, is the general lesson of the interference and diffraction observations which, as we have seen, occupy so large a part in modern physics? It is that, whatever light may be, it is something which passes through empty space with a perfectly definite velocity, and produces effects which show that it must have the alternating or periodic properties of waves.

A fundamental question, of great importance, arises. If light has the periodic properties of waves, how is it that optical problems of certain kinds can be successfully treated by considering light as travelling in straight lines? For calculating the ordinary behaviour of lenses and mirrors, for instance, we can in many cases safely take the paths of light beams as made up of straight lines, whose direction is changed according to simple laws when the beam is thrown back at a reflecting surface, or bent according to simple laws on passing through the surface of a transparent material. Shadows for ordinary purposes can be worked out by considering the light as travelling in straight lines from every part of the lamp or sun, those straight rays which meet the shadow-throwing object being stopped. But when ripples travelling out from a point over the surface of water or mercury meet an obstacle, say a round rod standing upright, they do not form a sharp shadow but spread into what the shadow of the rod should be, or if we put in the way an obstacle with a hole in it, the ripples passing through the holes spread out so as to make a wider beam than straight lines from the source of ripples would indicate. This it was that put Newton against considering light purely as a wave motion: he explained with a diagram that, if it were, then light passing through a hole should spread out into a wider beam.

The answer to the paradox has already been mentioned when we were considering ultrasonic waves. So long as the wave-length is very small compared to what limits the beam —to the obstacle, to the hole, or, as in the ultrasonic case, to the vibrating surface which is the source of the beam— then the error which we make by considering the wave motion as travelling in straight lines is very small and, if the wave-length is minute enough, can be neglected. For instance, for most purposes the behaviour of photographic lenses, consisting of several individual lenses, can be computed on the basis of what is known as geometrical optics, that is, on the basis of straight-line travel. When we come to consider, as we have been doing, very small or narrow sources of light, very thin sheets, very fine slits, in fact very small or narrow obstacles of any kind, and by very small we mean somewhere about the size of a wave-length of light, then wave properties come into prominence, and we can no longer use the methods of geometrical optics. The comparative size of wave-length and aperture or apertures of the instrument is what is decisive.

If I may interpolate here a personal reminiscence, during the late war an inventor who claimed to be highly qualified technically (and, in fact, appended to his name certain letters indicating a distinction to which I later found he had no title) came to see me about an invention of his involving a radio beam. To the question as to what wave-length he proposed to use he answered that it would be a few metres. When asked about the size of the parabolic mirror which he was going to use to produce the beam, he replied that it did not matter, but agreed that two metres diameter would be a convenient size when portability was considered. Anyone who proposes a parabolic mirror about a wave-length across to produce a parallel beam at once shows that he has no knowledge whatever of wave properties.

The general lesson is, then, that when the wave-length is very small indeed compared to any openings or, in general, to any dimensions that are in question, we can consider straight line rays: as soon as dimensions of anything like the wave-length are in question the various wave properties, in particular interference and diffraction, assume importance. It did not occur to Newton that the wave-length of light might be exceedingly small compared to the hole that he was considering, although he came so near to the wave theory of light that this is astonishing.

So far we have been talking about light visible to the human eye. However, just as there are air vibrations which are not audible, such as those caused by a plank oscillating two or three times a second, or, at the other extreme, the ultrasonic vibrations, similarly there are vibrations of the same nature as ordinary light which are not perceived by the eye. Beyond the violet there are shorter waves (or, putting it the other way, vibrations of higher frequency) which have a strong effect upon the photographic plate, and are known as ultra-violet rays. These are often depicted in popular literature as violet streamers, but, of course, as they cannot be seen they have no colour—they are not violet, but *beyond* the violet.

There are many different kinds of ultra-violet light, just as there are many different kinds of visible light, corresponding to different frequencies. The frequencies just higher than the visible violet pass through the glass of ordinary window-panes and camera lenses: they have a strong action on photographic plates. When somewhat higher frequencies are in question the rays do not pass through ordinary glass, although special glasses are made which transmit them. The rays which produce sunburn are a very narrow range of ultra-violet light of wave-length in the neighbourhood of three hundred-thousandths of a centimetre, as compared with the four or more hundred-thousandths of a centimetre that are the shortest wave-lengths visible. These rays not only do not pass through ordinary window glass, but they are markedly absorbed by the atmosphere, so much so that in winter, when the sunlight has, on account of its greater slant, to traverse a greater thickness of atmosphere than it does in summer, practically none of them gets through. This is why it is that even intense winter sunlight does not produce tan and sunburn, as can be vouched for by Canadian lumbermen.

Shorter waves still are absorbed in smaller thicknesses of air, but can be photographed with special plates and quartz lenses, quartz being a material that is very transparent to the ultra-violet rays. These different properties of different kinds of ultra-violet light show us how careful doctors treating patients with the light should be.

Passing still further into the short-wave region, we come to waves which are absorbed even by a fraction of an inch of air, and can only be detected by special methods with apparatus pumped free of air. When, however, we come to waves shorter than three millionths of a centimetre the penetration begins to increase: we are approaching the ordinary X-ray region—the ordinary X-ray region because the very strongly absorbed rays just mentioned are often called 'soft' X-rays. For one of the most striking discoveries of the present century is that X-rays are of the same nature as ordinary light, their peculiar properties being a consequence of an exceedingly short wave-length.

The wave nature of X-rays has been proved in the same way as the wave nature of light—by making use of a 'grating' of regularly spaced lines. The structure of X-rays is, however, so fine, the wave-length is so short, that the lines of the ruled diffraction gratings by which the wave-length of light is measured are, generally speaking, altogether too widely spaced for efficient service. It was the discovery of the German physicist Laue that in crystals, in which the atoms are spaced in regular rows, we have a diffraction grating, ruled by Nature, suitable for demonstrating and measuring the wave-length of the X-rays. This discovery was speedily extended by Sir William Bragg and his son, Sir

Lawrence Bragg, who showed how, conversely, X-rays could be made to yield the most far-reaching information as to the structure of the crystals. It should, perhaps, be mentioned that recently it has been found possible to use artificially ruled gratings of a particular type to produce diffraction results with the X-rays of longer wave-length, the 'soft' X-rays.

The X-rays used by doctors for diagnosis have wave-lengths of a few thousand-millionths of a centimetre, while those used for curative purposes are shorter still. Finally, one class of rays from radium has the same properties as X-rays, but is of still shorter wave-length: these rays, the so-called gamma rays, have, in extreme cases, wave-lengths of less than a ten-thousand-millionth of a centimetre. The gamma rays represent the very shortest wave-lengths of which we can handle a source in the ordinary laboratory. They are at the same time the most penetrating: even after they have passed through a plate of lead ten inches thick the effect of the gamma rays from radium and its products can still be detected. However, gamma rays of even shorter wave-lengths and greater penetrating power have been produced of recent years by the gigantic particle accelerations described later and have been detected in nature as a consequence of cosmic ray reactions. Cosmic rays are discussed in Chapter IX.

A fundamental feature of all the waves that we have been discussing is a very rapid oscillation of electric force. The general reason that such radiations are absorbed is that matter is built up of atoms which are themselves structures of electric charges, kept in equilibrium positions by internal electric forces. Such charged particles respond to the periodic electric pulls and pushes. Each kind of structure—each kind of atom and each kind of molecule built up of atoms—has its own pet periods of vibration and therefore responds particularly readily to forces of certain frequencies. These frequencies depend both on the particular structure and on the particular method of vibration in question. Thus, to take a rough illustration, when we considered a string we saw that it could vibrate either crosswise or lengthwise, and in either case with several distinct frequencies, according to the number of vibrating segments into which it divided itself.

Atoms themselves, consisting as they do of charged particles, have in particular different possible modes of vibration. If they are very sparsely scattered, as in a gas, their frequencies of vibration, and so of response, are pretty sharp: if they are tightly packed, as in a liquid or a solid, they disturb one another, with the result that they will answer more or less to any frequency in a certain range, responding most strongly at the middle of the range.

Most forms of matter have possible frequencies in the range of visible light, which means that they absorb waves in this region and are opaque. Metals in any thickness are opaque to a very wide range of frequencies, because of the 'free' electrons which they contain. Some solids, however, like colourless glass and colourless crystals, have no favoured frequencies in the visible range and so let practically the whole white light through: others have, in this range, certain frequencies of response only, so that they absorb some regions of visible light, but not others. These are transparent coloured bodies. Similarly, in the ultra-violet some bodies respond to frequencies in one region, others to frequencies in another: there are clear glasses made especially to transmit ultra-violet and others to stop it as much as possible. But when we come to penetrating X-rays or gamma rays, the frequencies of oscillation are so rapid that there is very little particular response to these frequencies by the charges in any form of structure. The X-rays of longer wave-length, the so-called 'soft' X-rays, are, on the other hand, very heavily absorbed, in a certain region of wave-length even by air, since the corresponding frequencies are well represented in the natural vibrations of the charges in all bodies.

So far we have been mainly considering waves of higher frequency and shorter wave-lengths than visible light. On the other side of the visible spectrum, beyond the red, lie invisible infra-red rays, which can be detected by their heating effects. A kettle of boiling water in a dark room gives out no visible light, but if it be raised and the hand be placed at a little distance underneath it (so as not to be affected by the hot air rising from it), heat will be felt which is due to invisible radiations. The infra-red radiations do not affect ordinary photographic plates, but special plates which are sensitive to them can be made, and, as a matter of fact, it is recorded that a hot kettle has been photographed in a perfectly dark room by the invisible heat radiations which it gives off, a considerable technical feat. Of course, ordinary light radiations, if strong enough, also produce a distinct heating effect: with sunlight the greatest heating effect lies in the visible yellow. With the infra-red radiations, however, the heating effect assumes particular prominence because it is the property by which they are most easily detected. The heating effect of the ultra-violet rays, in the intensity in which they ordinarily occur, is too small to be conveniently measured, but it also exists.

At still longer wave-lengths than the infra-red we come to the kind of electromagnetic waves which are used in radio-communications of all kinds: wireless telegraphy, broadcasting, television and such devices as radar, which deals not only with the location of aeroplanes but also that of other flying bodies such as meteors, by day as well as by night. The wave-lengths in question range from thousands of yards, used in certain types of broadcasting and telegraphy, through hundreds of yards, as used in medium-wave broadcasting, down to yards used for radar and television. To-day intensive work is being carried out on radio waves inches in length, for use in radar and for other purposes. Even shorter waves have been produced and, in fact, the gap between the longest infra-red waves produced by heat and the shortest radio waves produced by electric circuits has been bridged.

From what has already been said it is clear that with inch waves ordinary optical methods can be used, because mirrors and lenses many inches, or even feet, across are quite practicable. These lenses are made not of glass, but of some plastic material. Thus with such waves we can use telescopes made on the same principles as the familiar telescope for visible light. But what are ordinarily called radio telescopes are quite different instruments and bring us to one of the most exciting developments of modern science, which is radio astronomy, or the study of the heavens by means of the radio waves which reach us from outer space.

Quite apart from the cosmic rays, with which we deal later, it is probable that the heavenly bodies, of one kind and another, send out a very wide range of electromagnetic waves, including, besides the visible spectrum, ultra-violet and infra-red radiations of all wave-lengths. The atmosphere, with its electrified layers, however, is a great absorber of radiation and acts as a protecting coat which has only two 'windows': it lets through a band of frequencies, which includes visible light, of wave-lengths from about three hundred-thousandths of a centimetre, in the ultra-violet, to somewhere about one ten-thousandth of a centimetre in the infra-red and, further, a band of frequencies in the radio region, of wave-lengths from about 1 centimetre to 50 metres.[5] However, the main rays detected from outer space are of wave-length in the neighbourhood of 1 metre and special apparatus must be constructed if it is desired to cope with such radiation.

Our radio telescope, to give an approximately correct direction, which is the same thing as to give an approximately correct image, of a radio source must have a diameter of a few tens of wave-lengths. It may be noted that an ordinary optical telescope, with an objective lens 1 inch across, has an aperture about 40,000 wave-lengths of orange-coloured light, so that to get the kind of accuracy that such a telescope gives with the eye we should want a lens or mirror about 50 miles across with waves 2 metres long, and for the accuracy of performance of a large astronomical reflecting

[5] In inches one range of wave-lengths that get through is from 1.2 to 4 hundred-thousandths of an inch and the other range from 0.4 inch to 55 yards. A cigarette paper is about a thousandth of an inch thick.

telescope a radio telescope thousands of miles across would be necessary.

Such dimensions are, of course, out of the question. As typical of a practical radio telescope we may take that set up by A. C. B. Lovell at Jodrell Bank, near Manchester, to be completed in 1957. It is a steel radio mirror, of paraboloid shape, 250 feet across, which has been designed to work with wave-lengths down to 1 metre, and may possibly be also used with somewhat shorter waves. It will fix the direction of a celestial radio-emitter to something like half a degree, the accuracy, of course, varying with the wave-length: with it the 'radio-image' of a point, such as a star appears to be when seen through a visual telescope, will be about the size of the sun as seen by the naked eye—that is, an optical telescope of corresponding accuracy, or inaccuracy, would show for the image of a star a blur as big across as the sun appears to be without a telescope. It is all a question of the relation of wave-length to aperture. Another type of radio telescope is more like the Michelson stellar interferometer, already described, and consists of two receiving aerials not feet apart, but hundreds of feet apart. The signals received at the two stations are overlapped to produce an interference pattern, something as in the optical case.

This is not the place to describe the intriguing results obtained with radio telescopes, which were brought in here to illustrate how the same simple wave properties turn up in all branches of physics, but perhaps a word may be said, to indicate the nature of the possibilities. It has been found that strong radio beams come in from certain particular directions in outer space. These are put down to origins called 'radio stars', but there are no conspicuous visible stars in the neighbourhood of these sources of strong radio emission. Except for the sun, which is a strong radio-emitter, no visible star has been caught sending out radio waves. We are dealing with dark stars.

Most of the radio stars appear to be in our galaxy, but there are others outside it. In particular, the Great Nebula in Andromeda has been identified as a source of radio waves. Intense research is going on in England, at Manchester and Cambridge, and in Australia, at Sydney, which will, it is hoped, elucidate the nature of the cosmic catastrophes outside our galaxy that lead to these great emissions of long waves.

We have, then, using the word in a general sense, a spectrum stretching without a break from wave-lengths of hundreds of yards down to less than a ten-thousand-millionth of an inch, of which vast range only a very small region can be detected by the eye. Calling an octave a band of radiation stretching from a given frequency to double that frequency—for in sound a note has double the frequency of that an octave below it—we may say that our complete spectrum comprises sixty octaves, of which only one is visible.

What are the properties which all these waves have in common? Two characteristic wave effects are interference and diffraction, already discussed in connection with visible light. These have been demonstrated with gamma rays and with penetrating X-rays by making use of the regularities of crystals, the natural even spacing of the atoms in such structures taking the place of the artificial ruled gratings used with ordinary light. With soft X-rays already mentioned and with ultra-violet waves ruled grating can be used, with certain modifications of method. For long infra-red waves reflexion methods have been employed to show interference. These methods, suitably adapted for the different classes of radiation, and many others all show the same thing, the regular periodicity associated with wave nature.

The wave nature of radio waves was early demonstrated with structures of wires, but received striking confirmation in Appleton's experiments on the electrified layer known by the names of Kennelly and Heaviside, since in 1902 Kennelly in the U.S.A. and Heaviside in England independently pointed out that if the upper atmosphere were in an electrically conducting state it would reflect radio waves and so explain why the waves of wireless telegraphy did not escape into outer space, as it appeared mathematically that they should do, but went round the world, a thing that was puzzling the physicists at the time. In his work Appleton necessarily assumed that the radio signals had the properties of electromagnetic waves and the nature of his results proved the correctness of the assumption.

His early experiments were based upon the simplest interference considerations. Suppose two stations distant by many—actually seventy—miles. If there is a reflecting layer high up, acting as a horizontal mirror, waves sent out by one station can reach the other by two paths, differing in length, one direct and the other reflected. If the difference in length is an exact number of wave-lengths the waves will reinforce one another: if it is an odd number of half wavelengths the waves will cancel. Clearly with fixed distances everything will depend upon the wave-length. The method used was to vary the wave-length steadily: it was found that the received signal waxed and waned in strength, just as anticipated. From the distance of the stations and the wavelengths that gave maximum—or minimum—effect the height of the layer could be calculated and was found, in these early experiments, to be about 60 miles.

This kind of interference of direct and reflected waves is responsible for many of the peculiarities of short-distance wireless transmission known as 'fading'. It has been established by Appleton and his collaborators in England, using a method devised by Breit and Tuve in the U.S.A., that there are various layers in the ionosphere, as the electrified region is called, since ions are charged particles and it is to such particles that the reflexion is due. These layers comprise the E, or Kennelly-Heaviside, layer, the F, or Appleton, layer and minor divisions. The ionization is due to ultraviolet light from the sun and most interesting effects have been established, including daily and seasonal variations of the 'window', alluded to when radio astronomy was mentioned, and effects connected with the earth's magnetic field. A particular interest of the work in the present connection, however, is that it shows the wide scope of interference methods and illustrates the generality of the ideas of modern

physics. Principles established to account for the colours of
thin films and such-like puzzles of the physicist's laboratory
turn up unexpectedly in connection with the electrical properties of the earth's atmosphere and prove to have great
practical importance.

All the different kinds of waves which have been mentioned have the same velocity in empty space, which suggests their common nature. They are, in fact, all electromagnetic waves. The thing that varies periodically is the
electric force at right angles to the direction in which the
wave is travelling: accompanying the variations of electric
force we must, by the fundamental laws of electromagnet-
ism, have fluctuations of magnetic force, also at right angles
to the direction in which the wave is travelling, and at right
angles to the electric force. Thus, if a wave is travelling
across the page from left to right, there will be an electric
force in the direction from top to bottom of the page, say,
which first points up and then points down, diminishing
smoothly to nothing and then growing in the opposite direction in the course of each oscillation, while the magnetic
force will be at right angles to the sheet of paper, and will
fluctuate in a similar manner. We can therefore speak of
our general spectrum as the spectrum of electromagnetic
waves, ordinary light being electromagnetic waves within a
particular range of wave-length.

If this is so, we should expect to be able to demonstrate
experimentally electrical and magnetic effects with ordinary
light. Long ago, Faraday, the prince of experimenters, who
was convinced, by that instinct for scientific truth which he
possessed ('He smells the truth', said a great German scientist of him), that there was a connection of this kind, showed
that a magnetic field exerted a certain effect on light passing
through heavy glass. This effect, known as the rotation of
the plane of polarization, is somewhat too complex to explain in a short sketch of this kind. Likewise we can only
cite the effect named after the Dutch physicist Zeeman, who
discovered that the light from a source placed in a strong
magnetic field was modified in a peculiar way as compared

to light from the same source without the magnetic field. There is, however, a connection between light and electricity, the general nature of which can be simply understood, and which has, moreover, assumed the greatest importance of recent years. It is called the photoelectric effect, and has most notable practical applications as well as deep theoretical significance.

The photoelectric effect occurs in its simplest form when light, more particularly light of short wave-length, falls on a clean metal surface, say a plate of carefully polished zinc. The plate then loses negative electricity and so becomes positively charged. While the earliest experiments, which led to the discovery of the effect, were carried out in free air, to obtain accurate and unambiguous results it is necessary to work in a vacuum, which avoids various complications. By fundamental experiments with metal plates in exhausted tubes it was shown that what actually happens is that electrons, the little atoms of negative electricity discussed in the next chapter, are released from the metal by the action of the light. The stronger the light, the more electrons leave the plate every second. One aspect of the effect, of very great theoretical importance, is brought out when the quantum theory is discussed later.

The effect finds practical application in the so-called photoelectric cell. The simple cell consists of a surface coated with a suitable light-sensitive metal and some kind of wire electrode, sealed into an evacuated glass bulb, the wire electrode being there to conduct away the electrons freed by the light falling on the metal surface. A voltage is applied so as to make the sensitive metal area negative with respect to the other electrode, and so produce a small current when the light is incident, a current that is larger the stronger the light. In the early cells simple metals, such as potassium, rubidium, and caesium, were used, often coated on part of the inner glass surface, but to-day cathodes of more complicated composition, such as those built up of silver, oxygen, and caesium, are favoured, because they are much more sensitive to light. Such photo-cells are widely used in connection with television and talking films, since by their aid fluctuations in light can be turned into fluctuations of electric current, which in their turn can be turned into sound.

To take the case of the film, the original sound from actor, orchestra, or what-not can, by means of a microphone arrangement, be made to produce electric currents of corresponding frequency and strength. These electric currents produce, in their turn, corresponding fluctuations of light from a special discharge lamp. This light, of rapidly varying strength, is made to produce a band of varying grey, from light to dark, at the side of the film, the so-called sound track. A concentrated beam of light passing through this track varies, then, in strength, in a way corresponding to the variations of air pressure that constituted the original sound. What is required is to make this very rapidly fluctuating light produce sound.

It is here that the photoelectric cell comes in. The light, falling on the cell, causes fluctuations of the current from the cell: these currents are very small, but they can easily be magnified to any desired extent by modern valve-circuits. The magnified currents are led through some form of loudspeaker and a reproduction of the original sound is the result. The process depends upon the effect of light in releasing electric charges from metals, an electrical effect that, from the point of view of pure science, helps to establish the electromagnetic nature of light.

There is, incidentally, another way of making the sound track which results in a black band of varying width, but here again the strength of a beam of light passing by the strip is made to vary, and thus to produce sound in the way just described. The general principle is the same.

So far we have considered the number of electrons liberated, which depends on the strength of the light. This is, however, only one aspect of the question; another is the speed, or energy, with which the electrons are released from the metal. Strangely enough, this is not influenced at all by the strength of the light, but only by the frequency. Blue light liberates electrons with small energy of motion; violet light produces electrons of somewhat greater energy; ultraviolet light causes the emission of faster electrons still; while with X-rays the electrons expelled have a still greater energy. The energy which is imparted to each electron before it leaves the metal is, in fact, proportional to the frequency of the light. This is a very fundamental and important fact for modern physics.

Let us look at it from another point of view, not the production of electrons by the action of light or other electromagnetic waves on a metal, but the production of electromagnetic waves by the impact of electrons on a metal. Suppose that we make the electrons hit the metal with a given energy, which we can do by liberating electrons from a hot wire, as in the ordinary wireless valve, and then speeding them up with an electric field, just as, in the old game of bat, trap, and ball, we first make the ball jump from the trap and then slam it with the bat. When high speed electrons strike a metal plate X-rays are produced. The whole process must be carried out in a highly exhausted tube, where there are very few air molecules present to get in the way of the flying electrons and make them lose their speed: such a tube is an X-ray tube, as used in hospitals. If, by using a great voltage, we make the electron fly very fast, and hit the metal with great energy, very penetrating X-rays ('hard' X-rays, as the doctors call them) are produced—that is, waves of very small wave-length and high frequency. If the electrons strike the metal with less energy the X-rays produced are of longer wave-length, and correspondingly smaller frequency. Suppose, again, that we send a stream of electrons which, by comparison, are very slow and have small energy, through a gas, then we produce waves which are so much longer than X-rays that they are visible light: this is what happens in the tube with the pink glow used in advertisement signs, the neon tube.

In each case sending a greater number of electrons does not alter the frequency of the waves produced, but merely makes them stronger: we get a brighter light or, in general, more intense radiation. It is as if, in sound, the note of a gong should depend upon the violence with which we struck it a blow, being higher the more violent the blow, while the strength of the sound depended upon the number of blows. The whole point is that, apparently, the energy which is needed to produce a *single* train of waves of any kind of 'light' depends upon the frequency of the light produced, while, if a single train of light waves produces an electron from an atom, the energy of that electron depends upon the frequency of the light. This queer fact lies at the basis of the quantum theory, which is discussed in Chapter VII. It is introduced here merely to show that there are certain aspects of light which are not of the kind which can be explained from the simple wave theory, for this theory alone would not lead us to suppose any relation between the frequency of a single set of waves and its energy.

There are other electrical effects of light which have been widely applied. If light falls on a film of the element selenium, prepared in a certain way, the resistance of the selenium to electricity is diminished, and hence, if we have the selenium joined up with a battery, a bigger current flows, which can be magnified as much as we like by the technique of wireless valves. If the light is made to fluctuate, the current will fluctuate in a corresponding way, so that clearly we can use a selenium cell to turn light, made to vary in the proper way, into speech, just as we can use a photoelectric cell. However, whereas the response of the photo-cell to variations of light is instantaneous, with the selenium cell there is a slight lag, so that it is seldom used for this purpose. There are, however, many other practical uses of the selenium cell. In some cities the street lights are turned on automatically by the aid of selenium cells: as soon as daylight fails the resistance of the cell goes up, and a consequent change of current is made to operate a switch. Burglar alarms can clearly be operated on the same principle: as soon as light is made in a dark room a bell rings.

Selenium cells are called photo-conductive. Other photo-conductive cells can be made with films of lead sulphide, or selenide, or telluride, which likewise change their electrical conductivity when radiations fall on them. They are not very sensitive to visible light, but have the advantage that they respond well to infra-red rays, especially far infra-red rays, to which the ordinary photo-cells do not react. All these variations and applications are very interesting, but for our present purpose the great thing to be noticed is that light, visible and invisible, is a manifestation of fluctuating electric force which can be made to produce obvious electrical effects.

The study of light, then, like so many other parts of physics, seems to be the study of energy, the study of waves, and the study of electricity. There are three interconnected aspects of the same thing. At one time we fix our main attention on one, at another time on another, but they cannot be considered independently. If we understood fully any one part of physics, we should understand all of it.

# CHAPTER V

## About Electricity
## and Electrified Particles

THE word electricity derives from the Greek *electron,* amber, for it was known in classical times that amber, when rubbed, acquired the property of attracting light bodies, such as morsels of straw or scraps of feather. We say to-day that the amber becomes charged with electricity, and we know that if we support any body, say a metal plate, on an insulating stand, we can communicate part of the charge to it by simply stroking it with the electrified amber. If we hang up two light balls by silk threads, which do not conduct electricity, and charge them each by means of a piece of electrified amber (or sealing-wax or glass, for these bodies, and many others, become electrified when rubbed), they will repel one another if brought close together, so that we say that two electric charges of the same kind exert a force of repulsion on one another.

It is found, however, that if a rod of sealing-wax is rubbed with a woollen cloth, and then used to charge a small ball with electricity, while a second ball is charged with a glass rod which has been suitably rubbed, the two balls then attract one another. This shows that there must be two different kinds of electricity, for, taking a charged ball, we can, by suitable choice of the electrified substance, charge a second ball either so that it attracts, or so that it repels the first ball. If the two balls be charged with the same kind of electricity, either glass or sealing-wax electricity (to call them so for the moment), they repel one another; if they be charged with opposite kinds of electricity they attract one another. The two different kinds of electricity are always generated when a body is electrified by rubbing, for if the body, say a glass rod, acquires a charge of the one kind, the cloth acquires a charge of the other kind, and, as can easily be shown by experiment, in equal quantity. The process of rubbing does not then, on the whole, produce electricity, but separates out the two kinds in quantities just sufficient to neutralize one another completely if they are brought together again.

The two kinds of electricity, distinguished by the sense of the force which they exert on one another, are always spoken of as positive and negative electricity, terms originally introduced by Benjamin Franklin. Glass, or vitreous, electricity is called positive and sealing-wax, or resinous, electricity negative. There is no particular reason for the allocation of 'positive' to the one kind of electricity rather than to the other, but, once the arbitrary choice has been made, we stick to it.

It is well known to everybody that when we join the poles of an electric battery of any kind, say an accumulator, by a metal wire, an electric current flows through the wire. By this we mean that the wire acquires special properties. It exerts a force on a magnet brought into its neighbourhood and it grows warm: if the wire is a very good conductor the heating effect is small, but nevertheless exists, while if the wire has a high resistance the heating is very obvious, as in an electric lamp or electric radiator. Further, if the wire be cut, and plates attached to each end, and these plates be then immersed in a solution of a metal salt, a chemical action takes place, as exemplified by the separation out of the metal in the familiar silver or nickel plating baths. We therefore say that an electric current has a heating, a magnetic, and a chemical effect.

In the old days it was customary to distinguish between the current electricity produced by a cell, and frictional electricity produced by rubbing a glassy or resinous substance: they were spoken of as different things and called voltaic electricity and static electricity. We know now that all the properties of an electric current are produced by electric charges in motion, as has been shown by rapidly rotating an electrically charged disc. This fundamental experiment was carried out by Rowland of Baltimore in 1889. It proved what had long been believed, that electric currents are merely moving charges, just as water currents are merely moving drops. The moisture in a sponge and the liquid in a river are the same thing, water, but the properties which a river has of turning a mill wheel, wearing away the bank and so on, are consequences of the motion. In the same way electricity in motion produces effects which stationary electricity does not. Exactly how the electric charges pass along the wire we do not yet know, or, as the conventional man of science would say, the mechanism of the metallic conduction of electricity still presents difficulties.

There is a very close connection between electricity and magnetism. Just as there are two kinds of electric charge, there are two kinds of magnetic pole. One end of an ordinary bar magnet will always tend to point north, the other south. Two south-seeking poles (called south poles for short) or two north-seeking poles repel one another: a north and a south pole attract one another. This is merely a general analogy between electricity and magnetism, and does not in itself show any real connection between the two. But there is an actual interaction and it is hardly too much to say that the relationship between electric current and magnetic force is the basis not only of electrical engineering but of much of physics.

In the first place an electric current, that is a motion of electric charges, creates a magnetic force in its neighbourhood. This is a very familiar fact: the electromagnet, in which the magnetic force produced by a current is used to convert the iron core into a magnet, is a simple illustration. Another example is offered by the simple galvanometer, consisting of a pivoted or suspended magnetic needle sur-

rounded by a coil of wire, carrying the current to be measured. The strength of the magnetic force is used to measure
the strength of the current. Since a current exerts a force
on a magnetic pole, a magnetic pole must exert a force on
a current: which moves depend upon which is held and
which is free to move. In a galvanometer with a suspended
magnet the coil conveying the current is fixed and the magnet moves, but there is another form of galvanometer with
a fixed magnet, between the poles of which hangs a light coil
carrying the current to be measured. In this case it is the
wire carrying the current that is deflected. The current and
the magnet act on one another because moving charges produce a magnetic force.

But not only does a moving electric charge produce a
magnetic force: a moving magnetic pole produces an electric force, which can cause a current to flow in any circuit
of wires in the neighbourhood. The simplest example is
given by connecting the ends of a coil to a galvanometer:
movement of a magnet in the neighbourhood of the coil
produces a current. This electromagnetic induction, as it is
called, discovered by Faraday, is involved in practically every important bit of electrical apparatus. In a dynamo an
electric current is generated by turning coils of wire in a
magnetic field, which comes to the same thing as moving a
magnet towards fixed coils of wire. The changing magnetic
field may itself be produced by a changing current, which
will therefore generate or induce, as it is called, a changing
current in a neighbouring circuit with which the first current
is not connected; but it must be clearly understood that a
steady current produces a steady magnetic force, and so
cannot induce a current in another circuit near by. The induction of one current by another is utilized in the tele-
phone, in wireless telegraphy, in every form of television set,
and in countless electrical devices as well as in all heavy
electric machinery.

We have, then, the general rule that any movement of
electric charge creates a magnetic force, and that any movement of a magnetic pole creates an electric force. It was by

giving to these ideas, due to Faraday, mathematical form, and extending them from conducting wires to empty space, where electric and magnetic forces exist apart from any matter, that Clerk Maxwell came to the conclusion that if at any place we can produce oscillations of electric force (which must, of course, from what has been said, be accompanied by oscillations of magnetic force), these oscillations will produce electromagnetic waves which will travel out across empty space with the speed of light. This prediction was, as is well known, speedily realized by Heinrich Hertz, who demonstrated experimentally the existence of 'wireless' waves, although, of course, he never had any practical applications in mind. The development of wireless telegraphy as a means of communication first began after his death.

Every generator of electromagnetic waves is merely an apparatus for making electric charges rush backwards and forwards with a given frequency of oscillation in the wires of the sender, just as every source of sound is a vibrating material body. The moving charge has, as it were, a grip on what, for want of a better term, we call the ether of space,[1] and sends out its waves through this ether: the vibrating string or fork is in contact with the air, and sends out sound waves through it.

The general rules which govern the behaviour of electric charges towards one another, and the interconnection of electric and magnetic forces, do not, however, tell us anything about the ultimate nature of the electric charge, which, as far as they are concerned, might be something in the nature of a subtle fluid obeying certain mathematical rules —the 'electric fluid' of which old writers used to speak. Nowadays we know that such a term conveys a false impression. The natural unit of electric charge, the electron, the discovery of which transformed physics and ushered in the modern period, was revealed by the study of the passage

[1] The ether of space no longer has the material properties claimed for it at the beginning of the century (see Chapter IV), but it may still be used as a subject for the verb 'to undulate'.

of electricity, not through wires, but through the very attenuated gas in an exhausted tube. However, before the nature of the electron was convincingly demonstrated by experiments on the discharge of electricity through gases, its existence had been conjectured from a study of the passage of electricity through conducting solutions, the process named electrolysis.

If two metal plates stand in a solution of a simple salt and a battery of some kind is connected to them, a current passes through the liquid. If, for instance, the dissolved salt be copper chloride, the copper travels with the current to one plate, where it is deposited as a layer of metal, while the chlorine goes to the other, where it is liberated as a gas. The two components of the salt are thus made to go in opposite directions and are therefore named ions, from the Greek, meaning goers or travellers. Further, the ion that goes with the current is called the cation and that which goes in the opposite direction the anion: the plate by which the current enters is named the anode and that by which it leaves the cathode. Thus the anion goes to the anode, the cation to the cathode. This nomenclature was originally devised by Faraday, who first laid down the laws of electrolysis, in consultation with William Whewell, the philosopher and historian of science, who was something of a classical scholar, as were, at that time, most men holding prominent university positions.

Copper, and all metals forming part of salts in solution, furnish cations: chlorine, and other acid characteristics, such as the sulphate group of atoms, furnish anions. This electrically urged travelling of metal ions in solutions is, of course, the basis of electro-plating, the salts used being generally, for practical reasons, of a more complex nature, for instance, in the case of silver-plating, potassium silver cyanide.

Faraday's fundamental laws about electrolysis are, firstly, that the mass of substance taken to either electrode—say, for example, the mass of copper deposited on the cathode —is proportional to the quantity of electricity passing, that is, to current × time. Double the current, or double the time with the same current, gives twice as much copper on the cathode. Secondly, if the same current be passed through various solutions, the mass going to an electrode is proportional to the chemical equivalent weight of the substance. Thus the weights of silver and gold, deposited in separate cells by the same current flowing for the same time through both cells, are as 107.9 to 197.2, the ratio of the respective atomic weights. Both these chemical elements are monovalent: with a divalent element, such as nickel or zinc, twice the current is required, for reasons that will soon appear.

The basic laws of electrolysis can be simply explained on the supposition that, when a salt is dissolved, a proportion of the molecules—with certain salts practically all the molecules, if the solution be very dilute—spontaneously break up into ions, which are atoms, or atomic groups, with electric charges. Thus copper sulphate breaks up into copper ions, with a positive charge, and sulphate ions, which are sulphur-oxygen groups, with a negative charge. An objection made at the time when the theory was put forward was that, in the case of ordinary salt, sodium chloride, this would mean a break-up into sodium atoms and chlorine atoms. Now sodium metal reacts violently with water, taking the oxygen and releasing hydrogen, but nothing of the sort occurs when we dissolve sodium chloride in water. Hence, it was argued, sodium atoms could not be freed by the act of solution. That no chlorine gas is set free, even if the salt solution is boiled, is another aspect of the same difficulty.

This objection is cited because the answer to it brings out a very important point. It is not contended that sodium chloride breaks up into sodium and chlorine *atoms* but into sodium and chlorine *ions,* that is, positively charged sodium atoms and negatively charged chlorine atoms. This means, in terms of modern theory, sodium atoms that have lost an electron and chlorine atoms that have gained an electron. Chemical action depends essentially on the behaviour of the outside electrons of the atomic structure: tampering with these outside electrons changes the chemical properties. We now know that the neutral sodium atom has a complete shell of electrons plus one odd electron and that the chlorine atom has a complete shell minus one electron, so that the removal of an electron in the one case and the gift of an electron in the other case means in both instances complete electron shells on the outside of the atoms, that is, structures which are chemically inert. These details were not so clearly realized in the early days of electrolytic theory, but it was quite rightly contended that there was no reason to suppose that a charged atom would behave chemically like a neutral atom. An ion is, chemically speaking, a thing with its own properties.

It is now clear that Faraday's laws of electrolysis can be explained in terms of these charged atoms and atom groups. Any monovalent ion is associated with a unit charge, which it gives up when it reaches the electrode, returning to its normal neutral state and resuming its normal properties. Thus the quantity of electricity consumed, measured by current × time, is proportional to the number of carriers. It is natural, then, that the current should be proportional both to the amount of metal, say, deposited in a given time with any given solution, and to the atomic weight of the element for different solutions, when monovalent elements are concerned. This law is so rigidly obeyed that the international ampere is defined in terms of the metal which it can deposit: it is the unvarying electric current which, when passed through a solution of silver nitrate in water, in accordance with the authorized specification, deposits silver at the rate of 0.001118 gramme per second.

In the case of a divalent element it is only necessary to suppose that it carries a double charge, which is in accord with the general theory of chemical behaviour.

Historically, it was a consideration of the laws of electrolysis that first led to the belief in the atomic nature of electricity. Helmholtz, lecturing on Faraday's work, said in 1881: 'If we accept the hypothesis that the elementary substances are composed of atoms, we cannot avoid concluding that electricity also, positive as well as negative, is divided into definite elementary portions which behave like atoms of electricity'. Even earlier, Johnstone Stoney, likewise basing his argument on Faraday's law of electrolysis, had suggested that there must be a unit charge of electricity. From the number of molecules in a unit volume of gas at standard temperature and pressure, which was roughly known at that time, he even made a rough estimate of the size of the electronic charge. It was in 1891 that, repeating his conviction that there was a natural unit of electrical charge, he suggested the name of electron for it, which has been retained. Thus the electron received its name before it was ever isolated, just as helium received its name before it had ever been found and handled.

We now turn to the experimental demonstration of the electron as a free charge, electricity without an atom of matter. Suppose two rods of metal sealed through the walls and protruding into the interior of a glass tube: these rods may or may not terminate in plates of different shapes, according to the particular purpose of the tube. As in the case of conduction through liquids they are called electrodes, anode and cathode. As long as the air inside the tube is at the pressure of the atmosphere, quite a high potential difference, say 10,000 volts, can be applied to the electrodes without any spark passing. If now the air be gradually pumped out, a stage is soon reached at which the electric discharge sets in, first as a thick, furry-looking spark, and then as a beautiful glow, filling the tube with a sequence of striking and significant appearances which have been carefully studied, but must not detain us here.

When at length the air in the tube has been reduced to somewhere about a ten-thousandth of the original amount, the glass of the tube shines with a characteristic bright green glow. By introducing into the tube little screens of different shape it is easy to show that this glow is due to something streaming from the cathode, which strikes the glass walls. We cannot see the stream, but the glow which it produces when it strikes the glass enables us to follow the movement. If a magnet be brought near, the stream is turned

from its path, in just the same way as an electric curren
in a very flexible wire would be. A plate charged with elec
tricity also turns the cathode stream aside, again just as
the stream consisted of a number of little charges on whic
the electric force acts.

A study of the joint action of the electric and magneti
forces on the cathode beam led J. J. Thomson to the con
clusion that it consisted of a swarm of negatively charge
particles. Further, he was able to find the ratio of the charg
to the mass of each particle, since the charge is a factor i
the force acting on the particle and the mass is a measur
of the difficulty of deflecting the particle from its path. Usin
both electric and magnetic force makes it unnecessary t
know the velocity. With the ratio of charge to mass known
the mass can be found if the charge can be determined. Thi
charge was found by experiments that will be described
little later. They show that it is exactly the same as th
charge which we find associated with a monovalent ator
when we pass a current through a liquid. No experimen
has ever led to the discovery of any smaller charge, and
further, no matter what gas we have in the tube, the size o
the charge on the particle is always the same. The ultimat
unit of negative charge, free in the gas discharge and boun
to atoms in the electrolytic cell, is the electron.

The first establishment of the properties of the electro
was mainly due to J. J. Thomson and his school and t
Lenard. The mass of the electron is exceedingly small, eve
in a world of littles: it is, for instance, but little more tha
a two-thousandth of the mass of the smallest and lightes
atom, the atom of hydrogen. The electron is not a tiny piec
of something material carrying an electric charge, it is a
electric charge pure and simple, just as a raindrop is jus
water. We are accustomed to find water contained in vessels
and electric charges sitting on, or coursing through, matte
but the electron and the raindrop are divorced from con
tainers. That the electron has any mass at all is another wa
of expressing the fact that it requires a force to set an electri
charge in motion, or, in general, to change the velocity o

an electric charge, as can be mathematically demonstrated.

The cathode stream in the exhausted tube is only one way of producing electrons from matter: what actually happens in the tube is that the positively charged atoms in it are banged against the cathode by the electric force applied, and knock electrons from it and from themselves. There are various secondary actions which, in the actual tube, complicate the appearance of things. Electrons can also be made to come out of any piece of metal by heating it: a red-hot iron rod, or a glowing platinum wire held near a charged electroscope will discharge it. The object of the glowing wire in the familiar thermionic valve is to produce a supply of electrons. Light or X-rays falling on a metal plate will also drive electrons from it, as mentioned in the last chapter. In short, maltreating an atom, either by banging it hard by other atoms, as we do when we increase the heat agitation, or shaking it violently by changes of electric force, or hitting it hard with a moving electron or other ultimate projectile, will make it yield up electrons. The impact of an atom or an electron on another atom is, of course, only a question of change of electric force.

It can be shown by experiment that the electrons produced by one method are the same in all respects as those produced by another method, and not, as might possibly be supposed, that one kind of electron comes from one metal and another kind from another metal. Whatever the source, whatever the method of production, the same quantity of electricity constitutes this minute unit of negative charge. How minute the charge is can be, perhaps, best described by stating that to carry the kind of current that flows through an ordinary electric lamp would require the passage of a million million million electrons every second. The ordinary small 50-ampere-hour accumulator stores a charge equal to that on a million million million million electrons. So small is the atom of electricity.

For some thirty-five years after the discovery of the negatively charged electron a positive charge not associated with matter had not been found, much to the astonishment of men of science. For instance, in 1910 J. J. Thomson wrote: 'It is very remarkable that we have up to the present no direct evidence of the existence of positively charged particles with a mass comparable with that of the corpuscle', as he called the electron. At the beginning of 1933, however, the study of cosmic radiation by Anderson in America, and by Blackett and Occhialini in England, led to the discovery of a positive counterpart of the electron, namely a particle not associated with matter, possessing the extremely small mass of the electron and a charge of equal magnitude, but positive. Such a particle is called a positive electron, or positron. The existence of positive electrons was established by studying, with a Wilson cloud chamber in a magnetic field, as described later, the tracks of particles which the cosmic rays produce when they strike atoms. Positrons have, since then, been produced in other ways, and they have been very extensively studied. That they were never observed until so long after the discovery of the electron can be explained on theoretical grounds, for the calculations of Dirac lead to the conclusion that their free life is very short, that is, that they disappear by conjunction with a negative electron almost as soon as they are produced. Something more is said of these positrons later.

The positively charged particle which can persist in the free state, and with which we have long been familiar, is, however, an atom of hydrogen which has lost one electron. The atom of hydrogen in its ordinary neutral state has only one electron to lose, so that, when deprived of this electron, it constitutes the lightest positively charged atom of matter. It is further discussed in Chapter VIII, where it is explained that it is the nucleus of a hydrogen atom, and is called the proton. Its mass is about 1850 times that of the electron.

We now turn to the determination of the charge on the electron, which was the occasion of an experimental method that had profound consequences. When X-rays pass through a gas, such as air, they expel swift electrons from the atoms and these swift electrons in their turn release slower electrons from atoms through which they pass. Such electrons are picked up by other atoms, so that what is produced is, in effect, a swarm of positively and negatively charged atoms and molecules, a swarm of gaseous ions. Other agents are also effective in expelling electrons and producing ions, for instance ultra-violet light and swift atomic particles such as alpha particles.

Now charged particles of all kinds have a remarkable property which they share with dust particles: they act as centres of condensation for moisture contained in the gas in which they are suspended, as centres of assembly for water molecules. It was by taking advantage of this fact that the charge on the electron was first measured.

Air, or other gas, at a given temperature can normally hold a certain maximum amount of water vapour, which is then said to be saturated. If in any way more moisture is introduced, or if the air is cooled, it has more vapour than it can conveniently hold. The excess, if it comes out, takes the form of minute drops, forming a mist, but if there are no centres on which condensation can take place the air remains clear, although more than saturated—supersaturated —with moisture. If dust particles are present, or charged atoms, or free electrons, then each one becomes the assembly point of a tiny droplet and a fog is formed. The particles are said to act as a condensation nuclei, but the word used in this connection must not be confused with the atomic nucleus. The dust in the atmosphere and the ions produced by ultra-violet light in the upper atmosphere play a great part in the rainfall.

The easiest way to make moisture-saturated air become supersaturated is to cool it quickly and the easiest way to cool it quickly is to expand it, for just as air compressed (as in pumping up a motor tyre) becomes warm, air allowed to expand becomes cool. A large-scale example occurs when the saturated air in the monsoon from the Bay of Bengal blows against the steep edge of the great plateau of the Khasi hills, where Cherrapunji stands. This forces the air to rise rapidly and so, since atmospheric pressure falls with height, to expand rapidly. The consequence is that Cherrapunji has the heaviest rainfall in the world.

It is quite easy to produce a bottled cloud in the laboratory by suddenly increasing the volume of moist air in a vessel, using some form of piston device. If the air is made dust-free, but contains ions, produced by X-rays, say, a mist at once forms, consisting of a swarm of undivided drops. By a suitable expansion it can be ensured that condensation takes place on negative ions only. If, then, one can measure the total charge and also the number of droplets, the charge on a single negative ion, which is the electronic charge, can be found. Luckily, this numbering of the droplets, which sounds a formidable task, is possible in a simple way.

A very small drop falls at a uniform rate in air, owing to the resistances to motion which it experiences. Even a drop as large as a raindrop does not accelerate after it has fallen a short distance, but descends at a fixed speed—luckily, for a drop falling from half a mile without air resistance would have a speed of about 400 feet a second and so would be a projectile against which an umbrella would be of little use. The smaller the drop, the slower it falls, according to a fixed law, so that the rate of steady fall in air at a given temperature gives the size. With droplets of the kind in question, which are somewhere in the region of a ten-thousandth of an inch across, the rate of fall is extremely slow, somewhere about an inch a minute.[2] The rate of settlement of the flat top of the miniature cloud can therefore be made to tell the size of the drops. The total mass of the water condensed can be calculated from the properties of water vapour, and hence the number of drops can be found. The total charge is easily determined by electrical methods. It was on these lines that the charge of the free electron was first found by

[2] The clouds of the sky are, of course, subject to gravity and are falling all the time, but they consist of drops so small that, owing to the air resistance, the rate of fall is exceedingly slow, and in general they turn to rain before they reach the ground as cloud. In general, but not always, in mountains.

J. J. Thomson. It proved to be the same as the charge on the monovalent ions concerned in electrolysis.

Later Millikan, of Chicago, found the electronic charge more accurately by producing very small droplets of oil, or sometimes mercury, with a sprayer and letting them pick up ions, produced in the air round them by X-rays. These droplets were in a space between two horizontal plates and by applying an electric field could be moved up and down, or kept stationary against gravity. Their behaviour, under the given electric force, enabled the charge to be deduced. These experiments were particularly conclusive as to the atomic nature of the electric charge, since a droplet could pick up more than one charge: the charge, however, was always found to be a certain least value, corresponding to a single charge, or exactly two, three, four, or more times that value, never anything in between.

The property which charged particles possess of acting as centres of foggy condensation has been made by C. T. R. Wilson the basis of one of the most ingenious and sensational experiments in modern physics, which has had, and is having, most important application. It has already been mentioned in connection with the discovery of the positron. When the nucleus of an atom of helium, the so-called alpha particle, discharged by a radio-active element, say the particular element called Radium C, dashes through the air, which it does with a speed of about 12,500 miles a second, it knocks electrons out of the atoms wholesale, and leaves a litter of charged atoms along its path. Its path, like the path of a miniature tornado, is marked by a track of destruction, and our problem is to render the track visible. If the air, or for that matter any other gas, through which the rays are passing, is damp (or contains saturated water vapour, to use the more precise expression), and is then cooled by a slight expansion, part of the moisture wants to deposit, and utilizes the charged atoms or molecules as starting-points on which to build droplets, as already described. In the celebrated apparatus devised by C. T. R. Wilson the air in a cylindrical chamber, with a flat glass top, is suddenly expanded by the fall, through a controlled distance, of a hollow piston, coloured black to give good photographic contrast with the white tracks. This fall is produced by turning a tap which allows the air in the space under the piston to rush into an evacuated glass bulb. The tracks produced by the alpha particles shot across horizontally under the flat lid are photographed just after the expansion. A modified type of cloud chamber, introduced by Langsdorf, is often used today, in which the supersaturated region is continuously maintained by a layer of warm saturated vapour steadily diffusing downwards to the cooler bottom of the chambers. This is called a diffusion cloud chamber: the general principle is that of the original expansion cloud chamber of Wilson.

The result of the supersaturation, produced by the expansion in the Wilson chamber, is that the path of the swift atom is marked by a thin white line of fog, looking, against the black background which is provided, like a line drawn by a finely pointed white chalk. Each line actually consists of a string of tiny droplets. Swift electrons also produce charged particles along their paths, by knocking electrons out of the atoms which they meet, so that their paths are also made visible by this method. Since X-rays also throw electrons out of atoms with considerable energy, as was mentioned when the photoelectric effect was discussed, the path of a narrow beam of X-rays is marked, not by a single straight line, but by a tangle of white lines, each line being due to a swift electron released by the X-rays, which produces a track of its own. These tracks can be photographed and studied at leisure. The actual time of passage through the apparatus of the atom, electron, or X-ray whose effects are thus studied is, speaking generally, a thousand-millionth of a second or so; it is the damage which it leaves behind it that is utilized by the moisture and permanently recorded. The photographic exposure is timed so as to follow shortly after the expansion which reveals the tracks.

The information supplied by cloud chamber photographs can be powerfully extended by operating in a strong uniform magnetic field, which curves the paths of the particles. The amount of curvature gives the speed of the particles if the charge and mass are known and the direction of the curvature, to right hand or left hand when looking in the direction of the particle travel, gives the sign of the charge. It was with a cloud chamber in a magnetic field that the positive electron was discovered.

The result of work on the electrical properties of atoms and ultimate particles is to show that electricity, like matter, is granular in structure, the atom of electricity being a very small unit, the electron. Most electrical phenomena ultimately come down to the behaviour of electrons. The simplest cases, from the theoretical point of view, are those where the electrons pass in a beam through a nearly empty space, as in the cathode-ray tube, which forms the picture-making part of the television set. This beam, the movements of which cause the eventful glow on the viewing screen, follows closely the dictates of electric and magnetic forces: the apparatus is merely a very much improved and elaborated version of the tubes with which the properties and nature of the electron were first demonstrated. X-rays, as we have seen, are also generated in high vacuum, when swift electrons are suddenly stopped by hitting the atoms of a metal target. The glow in discharge tubes, such as the neon lamps used for advertising purposes and the sodium and mercury vapour lamps which, in one form or another, are such a lovely and lovable feature of modern life, is produced by the passage of electrons through gas at low pressure, and likewise involves the impact of electrons on atoms, but of comparatively slow electrons on atoms which are more or less isolated.

The study of any feature of the electric discharge in gas tubes or of the flames of the electric arc—or, for that matter, of ordinary flames—at once brings us to another aspect of electronic behaviour, the way in which the electrons of the atoms in question emit light. The emission of electrons by a glowing wire, which is their sources in cathode-ray tube and X-ray tube and electronic valve, is another feature of electronic theory. The liberation of electrons in the upper atmosphere by radiations from the sun, which is an aspect of the photoelectric effect, is not only the fundamental cause of the Kennelly-Heaviside and other electrified layers that surround the earth, but of the aurora borealis and of other phenomena of atmospheric electricity. A large part of the theory of the structure of the atom is concerned with electron behaviour. The electron is one of the essential keys to modern physics.

All electric currents in wires involve a consideration of electron movements, and so, for that matter, do 'wireless' waves, for the generation of such waves at, say, a broadcasting station is a matter of encouraging a mass-migration of electrons, first in one direction and then in the other, hundreds of thousand times a second, in the wires of the aerials. The general behaviour of streams of electrons *in vacuo* or in a gas tube may not be an altogether simple matter, but it is far less complicated than the question of their movements in a metallic conductor, even if the metal be supposed to consist of a single crystal and not a mass of minute crystals, which is the normal metallic state. Under the influence of the electric field—the potential difference that drives the current—there is a drift of electrons, but the thermal vibrations, the lattice structure of the crystals, and the quantum laws governing atomic structure, to be mentioned later, all play a part in making the theory of the current in solid conductors a very difficult question. As a rough, very rough, analogy we may take the movement of people streaming across an open space to some attractive building to correspond to the stream of electrons *in vacuo*, while their movement in a large modern city, with crowded and obstructed streets and with underground railways at different levels, where the trains are sometimes full and where changes from one line to another take place according to fixed rules, correspond to the passage of an electric current through a metal.

The complicated theory of the conduction of electricity in solids has been greatly developed in recent years and extended from metals to include the so-called semi-conductors, that is bodies such as germanium which conduct much worse than metals but better than what are ordinarily called insulators. Such semi-conductors have come into prominence as an essential part of transistors, little constructions of solid parts, not enclosed *in vacuo,* which can take the place of vacuum tube valves in television equipment, for instance. They are mentioned here as another example of an electronic conduction of a complicated kind.

We know that a current flowing round a circuit produces a magnetic field. A charge of electricity in motion is the same thing as a current, so that an electron moving round in an orbit of any kind will create a minute magnetic force, and be equivalent to a tiny magnet. The general magnetic properties of all substances can be explained, in fact, in terms of electrons circulating and spinning in minute orbits in the body of the substance, which respond to magnetic fields. The only substances which are popularly thought of as magnetic are iron and steel, but, in fact, all substances have magnetic properties. The elements cobalt and nickel possess the same kind of magnetic properties as iron in a marked, if lesser, degree, and are said to be ferromagnetic (from *ferrum,* the Latin for iron). The other elements are so much less magnetic than iron that it requires delicate measurement to show their magnetic properties. With some of them, the so-called paramagnetic substances, this slight magnetism is of the same kind as iron, so that, for instance, a piece of the substance, if exposed to a magnet, will try to approach it and move to the place where the magnetic force is the strongest; but others, the so-called diamagnetic substances, among which the metal bismuth is the best known, have opposite magnetic properties, in that they try to move to the place where the magnetic field is weakest. They are repelled by the pole of an ordinary magnet, instead of being attracted in the way to which we are accustomed with iron.

Many important features of the different classes of magnetic behaviour can be accounted for by the theory of the electronic structure of the atom, considered in Chapter VII. The simplest behaviour is always shown by matter which is in the gaseous state, and it is, in particular, the feeble magnetic properties of gases that are easiest to explain, for here it is the properties of the separate atoms that are mainly in question. When we turn to solids, and particularly to ferromagnetic metals which are what most people think of at once when magnetism is mentioned, things are very difficult. The magnetic properties of an alloy, in particular, bear little relation to those of the metals of which it is made up. For instance, alloys can be prepared which contain as much as 88 per cent of iron and yet are not at all magnetic, while other alloys, the Heusler bronzes, are nearly as magnetic as ordinary soft iron although they contain only metals which are not thought of as magnetic at all, namely manganese, copper, and aluminium. The special alloys now used to make exceptionally strong permanent magnets contain, in general, besides iron, metals which by themselves are feebly magnetic—thus alnico, a trade name, contains 54 per cent of iron but also aluminium (10 per cent), nickel (18 per cent), cobalt (12 per cent), and copper (3 per cent), and there are other highly magnetic alloys containing the same metals in somewhat different proportions. This shows that the electronic forces between neighbouring atoms are concerned. The chemical properties of a chemical compound bear little apparent relation to those of the components: the properties of sodium and chlorine are not obvious in sodium chloride, for instance. When electrolysis was under consideration it was pointed out that the atom and its ion behaved quite differently. In the magnetism of solids, likewise, interelectronic forces are what is concerned, including those between electrons in the complicated groups that are characteristic of the iron, cobalt, and nickel atoms.

That it is the structure of the metal, as well as its composition, that affects the magnetic properties, is clearly shown by the fact that these properties in an iron bar can be changed by heavily straining the metal. There is, further, a manganese steel, of a certain fixed composition, which may be prepared so as to be magnetic or non-magnetic. It is tough, ductile, and non-magnetic if it is heated and then suddenly quenched in cold water, but hard and magnetic if heated and allowed to cool slowly. There is another steel, wires of which can be changed from a non-magnetic state to a magnetic state simply by stretching them. The ferro-magnetic behaviour is but one of many characteristics that show that the properties of solids are extremely compli-cated, depending upon the internal crystalline forces pres-ent in the grains of which they are made up and conse-quently upon the way in which the crystalline structure has been deformed or modified by mechanical stresses or by heating, for instance.

Another strange fact which clearly proves that an interac-tion between the atoms determines the magnetic properties is that certain chemical components of iron, such as iron carbonyl, have opposite magnetic properties to iron, being diamagnetic and so shunning the strong magnetic field. A theoretical advance towards the understanding of the mag-netic properties of close assemblies of atoms has been made by Heisenberg, taking into account the influence of the spin of the electrons on the forces between them, a complicated question. Much has been done, but ferromagnetism remains one of the most intricate and intriguing problems of modern physics.

# CHAPTER VI

## About Solids and Liquids

THE inclusion of a chapter on solids and liquids in a little book on physics may seem, in these days, to call for some kind of apology. The reason that the solid and liquid state is not much discussed outside certain restricted academic and technical circles is, no doubt, that it is not generally considered so exciting as other aspects of the subject, and it is to some extent true that sensational discoveries have not been made recently in the field in question. The subject is, however, of great significance and offers an ample field for speculation and advance. If it is argued that it is unfashionable, well, fashions change. In fact, already there are signs of a change: the physics of metals is beginning to claim the attention of some of the best of the younger generation and has acquired the special name of 'metal physics', not known a few years ago. Even in the field of atomic research the physical properties of metals, solid and liquid, has assumed great importance, especially in the so-called piles, described later, in which controlled nuclear reactions are carried out on a large scale.

The subject is, by its nature, difficult. It might be supposed that the study of solids and liquids, familiar substances which can be seen and handled—hammered, bent, and broken; boiled, splashed, and poured—would be simpler than that of gases and, above all, than that of individual atoms, whose existence has to be argued from elaborate experiments. It is true that the rough properties of solids and liquids, as involved in domestic life, industry, and the arts, have been known for ages and that of recent times, with the immense growth of technology, their physical and chemical properties have been the subject of elaborate investigations, while in the laboratory their behaviour under a variety of conditions has been precisely determined. When, however, it comes to finding a physical explanation of this behaviour, to constructing consistent theories which shall describe quantitatively the measured properties, the task proves much more difficult than in the case of gases.

The reason is not far to seek. When we are dealing with gases at ordinary pressures and temperatures, we are concerned, as discussed in Chapter II, with molecules[1] travelling, between their collisions, in straight paths which are very long compared to their diameter. Thus the mean free path of air molecules under ordinary room conditions is about 300 times the molecular diameter. The molecules are, then, in close contact for a very small fraction of their history only and, for a satisfactory simple theory, all that we need to know about this fleeting contact is that it results in the molecules behaving as elastic particles, which rebound, rotate, and vibrate according to simple mechanical laws. The thermal and mechanical properties of gases can be calculated with some exactness from simple first principles.

Solids and liquids are, however, matter in the so-called condensed state, in which the distances between molecules are small compared with the size of the molecules. There is not much change of volume when solids melt: thus on fusion the volume of lead increases by about 3 per cent, gold by something over 4 per cent, and bismuth actually contracts by some 3 per cent. So the difference between the solid and the liquid state is not a question of the distance

---

[1] The term 'molecule' includes atoms in cases where the substance exists, as it does in the case of the inert gases, in a state where the characteristic particle is the atom. We may speak of monatomic molecules.

between the molecules. It is rather a difference of structure that is concerned.

All true solids exist in a crystalline state. In the case of such substances as quartz and rock salt, or, to take household substances, sugar and washing soda, the crystal form is obvious from the external shape, which is bounded by plane surfaces making certain typical angles with one another. In the case of metals it is less obvious, although large crystals of zinc can often be seen on the surface of galvanized iron. The crystalline structure of all metals can be revealed, however, by polishing a surface and treating it with an acid, or other suitably chosen chemical agent, or by exposing it to certain electrical or heat treatments. Examination under the microscope then shows the metal as a mass of minute crystal grains separated by boundaries made up, in general, of straight-line segments: it is the preferential attack on the boundaries that reveals the structure. In general the crystal grains are small, their size across being measured in hundredths, or even thousandths of an inch, but, depending upon the way in which the metal has been treated, they may be large enough to be easily visible to the naked eye, or, exceptionally, tenths of an inch across.

Even fibrous substances like wool and hair and cellulose have a regular structure of a crystalline nature. On the other hand, glass, although in the ordinary sense of the word a solid, does not normally show a structure of this kind. It also differs from well-marked crystalline substances, such as quartz, rock salt, and metals, in not having a proper melting-point. Whereas with crystals, steadily heated, a temperature is reached at which they abruptly become liquid, with glass, as with butter, the substance becomes steadily softer and softer, and although in the end it becomes a liquid that can be poured, at no particular temperature is there an abrupt change. Some authorities, therefore, refuse to call glass and such substances solids and regard them as very viscous liquids. In support of this view may be cited the fact that a long glass rod, supported horizontally at both ends, will, at room temperature, slowly sag under its own weight as time goes on, that is, will flow slowly under its own weight. Discs of pitch and rods of sealing-wax likewise flow very slowly under their own weight, although in the ordinary sense hard and brittle. Likewise pitch placed in a funnel will slowly flow out of it. Here, therefore, when talking of solids we propose to restrict ourselves to undoubted solids, of a crystalline nature.

The essence of crystal structure is a regular and systematic arrangement of atoms and molecules in space. As the simplest type of crystal structure we may imagine space to be divided up into equal cubes by three systems of parallel planes. If we now put an atom at the corner of every cube, we have the simplest type of cubic structure, as represented by rock salt, where as we go along any line of cube edges, sodium ions (for in this crystal the atoms are ionized) and chlorine ions alternate. In metals of cubic structure there is either, in each little cubic cell, an additional atom at the centre—the so-called body-centred structure—or an additional atom at the middle of each cube face—the so-called face-centred structure. For instance, sodium and all metals of its class are body-centred; gold, silver, and copper are face-centred. In certain other metals the crystals are built on a hexagonal pattern: in others, of which bismuth, already quoted as peculiar, is an example, more complicated structures are the rule.

Metals are, of course, relatively simple, since they consist entirely of atoms of one kind. With more complicated substances, built up of molecules containing two or more kinds of atoms—say quartz, where the molecule consists of one atom of silicon and four of oxygen; or copper sulphate, where the unit is an atom of copper, one of sulphur, four of oxygen, and five water molecules—the structure is necessarily in some ways more intricate. But there is always a typical cell, the arrangement of which is exactly repeated over and over again in a particular direction. A little space-plan formula will tell you where an atom of a given kind is to be found for a whole crystal. Of course, the atoms vibrate with the heat motion, and by the position is meant the average position, about which they swing.

In contrast, in a liquid there is no spatial order except that which is imposed by the fact that the atom cannot overlap. Given the position of one atom, the neighbours must be within certain limits of distance, but otherwise their position is unrestricted. The liquid corresponds to a very large number of balls turned out at random on to a billiard table, the solid to the same balls arranged in a systematic pattern. In some solids, for example those of the cubic face-centred class, the atoms are regularly packed as closely as possible. In such cases the liquid, at the same temperature, is bound to take up more room, as we have seen is the case with gold on melting. In other solids the structure, although perfectly regular, is rather loose, with systematically spaced voids. In such cases the liquid may take up less space, since when the regularity disappears the voids are as much filled up as any other parts. We have seen that such is the case with bismuth.

It has already been mentioned that X-rays are the agent used to determine the nature of the arrangement of atoms and molecules in crystals. Any regular series of parallel planes of atoms acts as a mirror reflecting the rays incident at a particular angle, giving, for a narrow beam, a spot on a photographic plate suitably disposed: the whole body of planes in a crystal gives a pattern of spots characteristic of the particular structure. The position of each spot depends on the angle which the beam makes with the characteristic planes of the crystal.

If the substance consists of a mass of small crystals, all angles are represented and the thousands of spots resulting make characteristic continuous circular arcs or circles, quite sharp. A liquid, owing to the liberty of the molecules to place themselves where they will, between limits, gives broad, ill-defined circles. The study of crystal structure by means of X-rays is a comparatively new branch of science, initiated by the Braggs, father and son. All the simple crystals have now had structures allotted to them: the investigation of the architecture of complicated crystals, such as those of proteins, is being hotly pursued to-day.

It might seem, then, that the behaviour of solids, with their regular structure, should be easier to account for theoretically than liquids. This is true of some properties, but emphatically not so of others, as we shall now discover.

With ordinary liquids—by which is meant any liquid of uniform and definite composition, such as water or acetic acid or benzene, as distinct from certain complicated mixtures, such as paints—the properties are known if the chemical nature of the liquid and its temperature are known. Thus in an appropriate book of reference one can find the optical properties, the heat properties, the electrical properties, and the mechanical properties, such as viscosity and compressibility, of benzene at 20° C. With a solid, however, there are two classes of properties. With one class, known as the structure-insensitive properties, the same is to some extent true. Thus, with a metal the density is roughly known, once the composition of the metal and the temperature are known, and the same is true of the specific heat. Roughly known, and not accurately known, as with a liquid, because the properties in question depend somewhat on the treatment that the metal has received. For instance, the density of metals may vary by 1 per cent or so according to whether they are as cast, or have been subsequently hammered, rolled, or otherwise mechanically maltreated. Still, these structure-insensitive properties can be looked up in tables and approximate values found.

Things are quite different with what are known as the structure-sensitive properties of solids, which include not only the mechanical properties but also, for instance, the magnetic properties. As the name suggests, with a perfectly definite solid at a definite temperature these properties depend to a very large extent upon details of internal structure, which in its turn is greatly influenced by the treatment that the specimen has received. This is particularly the case with metals. Examples have already been given, in Chapter V, of the influence of mechanical treatment, which modifies structure, on magnetic properties.

An extreme example is offered by metal wires or rods that have been prepared so as to consist all of one crystal, having the same directions of crystal axes throughout the whole specimen instead of consisting, as is normally the case with metals, of a huge number of crystal grains, each with its own orientation of structure. The single crystal wire is soft to an extraordinary degree, and with some metals, for instance cadmium, may pull out without breaking to a few times—up to five times in extreme cases—its original length. The properties depend, too, upon the direction of the crystal axis with respect to the axis of the rod. To quote a particular typical case, a load of one-hundredth of that required to produce marked permanent stretch in an ordinary cadmium wire produced a large permanent extension in the single crystal wire and a load less than that required to produce a noticeable stretch in the ordinary wire extended the single crystal wire to four times its length. The wire pulls out into a flat strip, showing a structure of finely stepped bands, much like those produced by pushing sideways the top card of a pack lying flat on the table. They are caused by marked glide taking place on a large number of parallel crystal planes. Hardening takes place as the wire is extended in this manner.

It is a commonplace of technology and metallurgy that preliminary mechanical treatment and heat treatment have a very great effect on the mechanical properties of metals. The same steel may be springy, soft, or brittle according to the heating and cooling processes that it has experienced. Extending, compressing, or shearing a metal will, in general, make it more resistant to deforming forces, a phenomenon which is known as work-hardening.

In general metals can be shaped—can be deformed, to use the more technical phrase—by forces of various kinds, such as compression, extension, and shearing stresses, if they are sufficiently large, and the higher the temperature the more easily is the change of shape brought about. Speaking very roughly, the higher the melting-point of a metal, the higher the temperature required to make it yield by a given amount under a given stress—thus iron at 500° C behaves, mechanically, something like lead at ordinary temperature —but, of course, small additions of other metals greatly affect the resistance to deforming forces. A good example of the plastic behaviour of metals at higher temperatures is that, in the case of copper, brass, and lead in particular, rods and pipes are commonly made by squeezing the heated metal, at very high pressure, through dies, in just the same way as macaroni and spaghetti are made.

But metals do not, as glass does, get softer and softer indefinitely as the temperature is raised. A point is reached when the metal, still quite solid even if it behaves like a very tough dough, suddenly becomes a liquid that runs like water. This sharply defined melting-point is, as has already been mentioned, characteristic of all metals and, in fact, of all crystalline structures. According to one school of thought, it is a characteristic of *all* solids, for any substance like glass, which has no melting-point, but softens continually as the temperature is raised, is, by this school, considered to be a very tough liquid.

Metals subjected to a large steady stress will very slowly flow, the movement being generally called 'creep'. The creep is, of course, very much more marked, with a given metal, at higher temperatures. Even very small creep is very serious in such structures as the turbine blades of turbo-jet engines, and much special research has been carried out to find alloys resistant to creep at the high temperatures in question. It has been shown that creep is of two kinds: with one kind, the main type at low temperature, the rate, under constant stress, decreases steadily as time goes on, so that the behaviour at a given moment depends on the previous history, while the other type of creep, characteristic of higher temperatures, proceeds at a steady rate. It is, of course, the latter that is particularly serious in most practical problems. Changes in the crystal structure of the metal which may take place during creep are one of the complicating factors.

Glancing at the queer properties of metals, which were little studied by scientists fifty years ago, we are met with another, the so-called fatigue. If a metal part is subjected to a rapidly varying stress, say, for definiteness, a small bending first in one direction and then in the other, after a certain very large number of alternations it will break, even although the stress is well below that which it can safely bear as a steady load. If, however, the stress is below a certain value, the *endurance limit,* the metal is safe, however long the alternations of stress have continued. What is in question in fatigue failures, such as have taken place in aeroplane components which have been vibrating, is many millions of cycles—in fact, tests are usually carried out for 10 million cycles.

The reason that these features of metal behaviour have been mentioned is that they take place with crystalline substances, which constitute the typical solid structures, but on any theory of a perfect crystal none of them is to be anticipated. The theory of the perfect crystal further shows that it should be very much stronger than any known metal. Moreover, it should behave elastically for quite large extensions, returning to its original form after being stretched by several per cent: it should either break sharply at a certain high stress or flow very rapidly to fracture, not creep. In brief, the mechanical properties of a crystalline substance, such as a metal, are quite unlike those to be expected of a perfect crystal, and the mechanical properties of a metal in single crystal form, as prepared in the laboratory, differ still more from the ideal than those of a metal in its usual, polycrystalline, form.

The reason for all these discrepancies is that real crystals are not perfectly regular in structure but contain small regions of misfit, usually called dislocations, a very appropriate term meaning, as it does, things out of proper position. An atom—to consider the simplest case of monatomic crystals, such as pure metals—in a regular lattice is strongly held in position: it corresponds to a ball in a deep smooth depression, which, if displaced, will return to its original position. The regular lattice will correspond to a regular pattern of such depressions, separated by smoothly rounded elevations. These depressions are, of course, in an imaginary surface and correspond to a field of force: they do not actually exist in the crystal. If atoms in a given small region are, in consequence of disturbances of the resultant attractive forces, so displaced from their regular equilibrium position as to be half-way or so up the sides of the hollow, it is comparatively easy to push them over the elevation and then the region of irregularity, the dislocation, will move forward. Slip on a crystal plane containing a dislocation takes place easily, then, as a consequence of the travel of a dislocation under stress. When the dislocation has passed from one side of the plane to the other the result will be the same as if the whole crystal on one side of the plane had been moved at once by one atom spacing with respect to the other half, but to produce this simultaneous movement in a perfect crystal would require a very large stress.

In an ordinary polycrystalline metal the slip in any one of the crystal grains of which it is made up stops at the boundary of the crystal grain. This is, roughly, why the polycrystalline metal is more resistant to mechanical forces than the single crystal. A metal can deform, however, not only by slip within the crystal grains, but by movement of the grains with reference to one another. The effect of grain size is, then, far from being a simple matter.

The often astonishing effect on mechanical properties of very small additions of other metals, or of carbon, as in certain steels, can be understood in terms of this theory. A foreign, ill-fitting atom may get into a dislocation and jam it. Foreign atoms built into the regular crystal lattice may distort it. Alternatively, foreign atoms may go, by preference, into the irregular region between crystal grains rather than enter into the crystal structure. The large effect of deforming the metal by rolling, forging, stretching, or other processes can, in general, be understood as being the result of such structural changes as the glide produced in the crystal grains, the change of direction of the crystal axes of the grains, the growth of certain grains at the expense of their neighbours, and so on. Heating leads to grain growth, migration of foreign atoms, and other structural changes. In certain cases, as with iron, the whole pattern of crystal structure changes at a certain temperature: at temperatures below 900° C or so the crystal structure is of so-called body-centred cubic form, above this temperature it is of so-called face-centred cubic form.

If pure metals, or metals with slight impurities, show such perplexing mechanical properties, the complications which are to be found in the case of alloys, especially alloys of three or more metals, can well be imagined. The general conclusion is that the properties are to be explained in terms of modifications of crystal structure and of crystal boundaries, such boundaries being regions where the atoms properly belong neither to one nor to the other crystal pattern. When structure-sensitive properties are concerned—and, generally speaking, all mechanical properties are structure-sensitive—crystal dislocations, their travel, healing, and blocking are at the bottom of everything. Taking a chain as a rough analogy, its mechanical properties are weakest-link properties, but such things as its density—weight per unit length—and specific heat are independent of the weakest link.

Ferromagnetism is likewise a structure-sensitive property. Examples of the way in which it may be strongly influenced by mechanical treatment of the metal have been given at the end of the last chapter. The theory of ferromagnetism is based upon the conception of crystal domains: in adjacent domains the magnetizations are in opposite directions when there is no magnetic force, and cancel one another as far as outside effects are concerned, so that the metal shows no magnetic properties. The application of a magnetic force promotes domains of one direction at the expense of those of the other, and so produces external magnetic phenomena. Needless to say, the theory is more complex than these few words might suggest: all that it is desired to do is to indicate how it is that strains in the crystal lattice may have a large effect on ferromagnetic properties.

The structure-sensitive properties of solids are a complication from which the liquid state is free. On the other hand, where structure-insensitive properties are concerned the solid state is simpler, this being a result of its more regular structure. We may take the specific heat as an example. In the quantum theory of this property each atom is regarded as oscillating about an equilibrium position with a certain frequency of vibration, all the atoms being arranged in a regular crystal lattice structure. At low temperature the average energy per atom is very much less than the quantum of energy pertaining to this frequency, which means that most atoms are not vibrating at all, since, on the quantum theory, an atom must either have a quantum of energy, or a multiple of this, or no energy at all. Consequently at these low temperatures a very small addition of energy will activate the small fraction of atoms which can possess a quantum of energy. The result is that the specific heat should be expected to be nothing at absolute zero and very small at very low temperatures, rising rapidly until a temperature is reached at which every atom has a good chance of receiving an equal share of energy, when the specific heat is constant. The specific heat of crystalline solids actually varies in this way. The harder a body, that is, the more firmly bound the atoms, the higher will be the atomic frequency, the greater the quantum of energy, and the higher the temperature needed for the specific heat to have its full value. This also is found: thus for diamond, the hardest of crystals, even at atmospheric temperature the specific heat has far from reached its full value.

The original quantum theory of crystals was worked out by Einstein: it was improved by Debye, who took account of the disturbing effect of neighbouring atoms on the vibration of a particular atom, and further by Born, who took full account of the lattice structure of the crystals. What is essential is that the theory demands that all the atoms shall be arranged in a regular space pattern, every one behaving similarly to every other one. Of course, in a dislocation region they would be slightly different, but the volume of dislocation regions is a very small fraction of the total volume, so that for this purpose they can be neglected, although when it comes to starting an avalanche of mechanical strain they are of supreme importance. For every thousandth link to be of half the normal weight would be of supreme importance for problems involving the strength of a chain, but of very little importance in calculating the weight of chain per hundred feet, or its specific heat.

When we turn to the liquid state we have, as already indicated, the great simplicity that the properties of a liquid, of definite chemical composition and at a given temperature and pressure, are definite, not affected by the previous history. It does not influence the behaviour of, say, water at 20° C if it has been kept for some days as ice before being raised to that temperature, or of pure alcohol at the same temperature if it has been repeatedly boiled.[2] The structure of the liquid cannot be modified by mechanical treatment. We have, however, the complication that the structure of a liquid lacks the regularity that that of a crystal possesses. The result is that the specific heat of liquids, for instance, cannot be accounted for theoretically with the precision which is possible in the case of solids: in fact very little is known about it.

Important mechanical properties of a liquid are the viscosity, or resistance to flow—internal friction, as it was formerly called in English and still is in German—and compressibility. As regards viscosity, it has been shown that the viscosity of very simple liquids, such as molten metals, can be calculated from the average frequency of vibration of the atoms, which are supposed to communicate motion at the ends of their swings, and the way in which viscosity varies with temperature has been mathematically expressed. In general, however, it must be admitted that whereas there is a satisfactory theory—which means, at bottom, a satisfactory picture—of the gaseous state and of the solid crystalline state, as far as the structure-insensitive properties are concerned, there is no generally satisfactory theory of the liquid state, a strange state of affairs when we think of the enormous advances that have been made in atomic physics. It

---

[2] Of course, that boiled water has some properties different from fresh tap water does not affect our point: the chemical composition is not the same, in that one specimen contains dissolved gases which the other does not.

is true that great ingenuity and outstanding mathematical powers have been applied, notably by Born and Green, to the problem, but the subject awaits some general simplifying hypotheses before the situation can be considered satisfactory. The general theory of gases is comprehensive and gives a very good account of the observed properties: the theory of the structure-insensitive properties of solids can claim wide successes: but the general theory of the liquid state is complicated and, with all its complications, gives a very incomplete account of liquid properties.

# CHAPTER VII

## About the Quantum Theory

MANY of the most exciting of the modern developments of physics have been bound up with investigations of the properties of the radiations which travel through empty space, and, in particular, with their relationship to matter. Such radiations, of which visible light is an example, are started on their voyage by some kind of minute electrical disturbance in matter, and their arrival on matter of any kind is always attended by electrical effects. Sometimes these electrical effects can easily be detected, as, for instance, the induction effects of the wireless waves of broadcasting and television, which are primarily electrical before they are converted into sound; the ionizing effect of X-rays on the gases through which they pass; or the photoelectric effect of ultra-violet light. In other cases, as in the passage of light through glass or water, there is no electrical effect of this obvious kind, although the action of a magnetic field on the light during its passage through heavy glass shows clearly what we should have expected from other considerations —that electrical forces are in play. Through the common friend, electricity, the behaviour of radiation is inextricably mixed with the properties of matter. The quantum theory, which is a theory of radiation initiated at the very beginning of the present century by Max Planck, has made its influence profoundly felt in every branch of physics—and many branches of chemistry.

To approach the theory we have to consider the question of the energy of radiation rather more closely than we have done hitherto, and, in particular, we have to make ourselves familiar with something known to physicists as a 'black body', which plays an important part in many questions of radiation. In the first place, however, it must be pointed out that surfaces which absorb radiation well send out plentifully the same kind of radiation if they are heated, while bodies that do not absorb well radiate very poorly themselves. For instance, any dull black surface absorbs practically all the radiation which falls on it, while bright tin, which reflects so well, can clearly absorb very little. If, now, two vessels of exactly the same size and shape—say quart kettles—be taken, one of iron which is covered with soot, and the other of bright tin, and boiling water be poured into each, the water in the sooty kettle will grow cold quicker than that in the other kettle, because more energy is radiated away by the black surface. Similarly, the best vacuum flasks, for keeping hot liquids hot and cold liquids cold, are always silvered: if the flask contains cold liquid, we have the advantage that the silver reflects radiation falling on it from outside, or, in other words, absorbs very little radiant heat, while, if the flask contains hot liquid, we have the advantage that the hot silver radiates very badly, so that very little of the heat is lost by radiation.

The ideal 'black body' of the physicist is one that absorbs completely every kind of radiation falling on it, and so must, if heated, radiate as much of every kind of radiation as possible, more than any other kind of body at the same temperature would radiate. Of course, we cannot coat a body with soot to make a black body of this kind, for the soot would burn off when the body was strongly heated. Certain metal oxides are black, and also resist heating, and so can be used to prepare a black surface, but theory shows that the best way to realize the ideal black body is to make a closed vessel of some heat-resisting material—of, say, iron, or, if higher temperatures are needed, of special porcelain —heat the vessel strongly from outside, and let the radiation come out from the inside of the closed vessel through a small hole.

In a general way it can easily be seen why this acts as a black body. We have seen that a perfect absorber becomes, if hot, a perfect radiator. A small hole in a hollow vessel, especially if the interior of the vessel be blackened, acts as a very good absorber, for the radiation which passes through the hole gets scattered about inside and never comes out again. For instance, an open window in a white housefront looks a perfectly black square on a sunshiny day: the sunshine is reflected from the white wall, which looks bright, but, passing through the hole into the room, is weakened at every encounter with objects there, especially if they be sombre or dirty, so that very little escapes again out of the window. The glowing heart of a furnace is an ideal radiator, for it is practically a small hollow surrounded by glowing bodies all at one high temperature.

The paradox of the term 'black body' appears when we consider what happens when we heat the walls of our iron vessel red hot, or even white hot. A bright light comes out of the hole, and yet we call this 'black body radiation'. All that is meant is that it is the kind of radiation which comes from a body that, since it absorbs all radiation that falls on it, presumably sends out, when heated, as much radiation of every kind as possible. The term 'complete radiation' or 'full radiation' probably expresses more clearly what is meant, but the terms 'black body' and 'black body radiation' are so widely used—and gives rise to so much misunderstanding—that this word of explanation has been offered. In short, a perfect absorber is a complete radiator and goes by the name of a black body.

Some very interesting questions arise in connection with the radiation from a black body. Since we have in such a hot body a source of radiation which has no prejudice in favour of any particular kind of light, red, green, blue, or invisible, for it absorbs all equally, we should like to know how it distributes its energy among the different possible wave-lengths, for that would clearly tell us something about the relation between matter and radiation, just as, if one had a completely unprejudiced finance minister in a country, the way in which he distributed money to the different State activities—so much to the armed services, so much for education, and so on—would tell us much about the relation between money and the State. When experiments are made, it is found that at every particular temperature the hot body sends out a whole range of wave-lengths, a whole spectrum. When the body is very hot—white hot—it radiates every kind of light in the visible spectrum: when it is only moderately hot—say at the temperature of boiling water—it does not give out any visible light (a kettle full of boiling water is not visible in a dark room), but nevertheless it does give out infra-red radiation.

There is a perfectly simple rule by which to understand the general nature of the changes in radiation that take place as the body is heated: the hotter the body, the more the short wave-lengths predominate. Thus a plate of heavily oxidized iron when at a temperature of 300° C is invisible in the dark: all its radiation is in the infra-red. When it is heated, the boundary of the radiation creeps towards the red, until, when it is about 500° C, some visible red is included, and the iron is feebly red hot. As it is heated still more, more visible rays are added to the spectrum of the radiation, and the plate appears orange and then yellow hot, and, finally, even a little blue is sent out along with the other rays, and the plate is said to be white hot, although the light which it radiates is much redder than sunlight. All the time most of the energy is in the infra-red, but the place of greatest energy tends to approach the visible spectrum. A plate of iron is not, strictly speaking, a 'black body', but behaves sufficiently closely to one to illustrate the point. A full radiator as hot as the sun gives out *most* radiant energy at the yellow region of the visible spectrum: a body immensely hotter would give it out in the blue.

Careful measurements made with full radiators in the laboratory show exactly how much radiant energy of each wave-length is sent out at different temperatures: at any one temperature they furnish a kind of census of the number of units of energy in the region of each given wave-length, just as a population census furnishes, for any one country, the number of people of each given age group. Different countries, where the distribution is different, correspond to different temperatures. Now, before the quantum theory was put forward, there was no notion of natural units of radiant energy: it was believed that we could have any amount of energy, as small as we pleased, radiated by a hot body or a luminous atom. It could, however, be shown mathematically that, if this were true, we should expect a hot body to radiate nearly all its energy in the violet and ultra-violet end of the spectrum, which we know to be against the facts of observation. No theory based on the older ideas gave any proper account of the distribution according to wave-length of the radiation from the unprejudiced radiator or 'black body', which became, at the end of the past century, the bugbear of the physicist.

The problem was solved in the first year of the present century, when Planck showed that, to get the right result, it was necessary to make a revolutionary hypothesis: to suppose that radiant energy was sent out in packets, as it were —in units or atoms of energy, just as matter existed in atomic units. We cannot have less than an atom of lead, say; any minute piece of lead must consist of a whole number of atoms. We cannot have an electric charge of less than an electron. In the same way, we cannot have less than a unit —or quantum, as it is called—of radiant energy, and any body that sends out or absorbs radiation must deal with one quantum or a whole number of quanta. Radiant energy is dealt with in grains, not in infinitely divisible quantities.

The little parcel of light of one particular frequency in which radiant energy is delivered is sometimes called a 'light dart', a very expressive term, but is more generally known as a photon, not to be confused with proton. The photon is simply a quantum of radiant energy, the only object of sometimes using the new term being that 'quantum' is a more inclusive term, which can be applied to other things as well as light—for instance, to the vibration of whole atoms and molecules.

The quantum of radiant energy differs from the quantum of electricity, the electron, in a very important way. The amount of charge is the same on all electrons: there is but one unit. The magnitude of this unit of radiant energy, however, is different for every different kind—that is, for every different wave-length—of radiation. It is, in fact, proportional to the frequency, so that the quantum of energy of extreme visible red radiation is only half that of the extreme visible violet radiation, which, as we have said before, has double the frequency. The quantum of an X-radiation is very much greater than the quantum of any visible radiation. It is as if we could only buy things in fixed quantities, but that the minimum quantity varied with different things: pumpkins by the pennyworth, peaches by the shilling's worth, gold rings by the pound's worth, diamonds by the ten pounds' worth. The unit of price, increasing as the size of the article diminishes, corresponds to the quantum of radiant energy increasing as the wave-length diminishes.

The quantum of energy corresponding to a given species of radiation is found, then, by multiplying the frequency by a certain fixed number, which is called Planck's universal constant, and always indicated by $h$. It is a unit of action, action being the technical name for a quantity which is a momentum multiplied by a distance: such a quantity when multiplied by a frequency gives an energy. Planck's constant enters into every aspect of modern atomic physics and its numerical value has been found by at least ten different methods, involving such things as X-ray properties, the distribution of energy in black-body radiation, the frequencies of spectral lines, and so on. All the methods give values agreeing to within a few parts in ten thousand.

Light, then, or radiation in general, has a packet property as well as a wave property, and this is one of the paradoxes of modern physics. Newton's conception of light was a stream of particles, which he endowed with something in the nature of pulsating properties in an attempt to account for certain phenomena which we can now easily explain on the wave theory. He felt the need for the double aspect, the particle and the periodic, and provided for it in his theory.

If white light could be considered to consist of particles of various sizes, corresponding to all the different colours which it contains, it would be fairly easy to imagine the amount of energy in each particle to depend upon its size, and the quantum, or atomic, nature of the energy would be a natural consequence. We could have one or two or three particles of sodium light, but not a fraction of a particle. However, to account for the various phenomena of interference and diffraction described in Chapter IV, we have to admit that light has wave properties. We are thus forced to believe that light behaves under some conditions as a stream of particles, each one of which has a fixed energy belonging to it, and under other conditions as a wave motion. Both wave aspects and particle aspects are included to-day in a comprehensive theory known as wave mechanics, of which something more will be said later. It is, however, a mathematical rather than a physically pictured scheme.

This theory gives wave properties to all forms of ultimate particle and does formally reconcile the wave and the quantum properties of radiation. For many purposes it is easier, and it is sufficient, to know when we can treat radiation, and the electron, for instance, as particles and when we should consider them as waves. This kind of situation arises not infrequently in science—thus in geometrical optics we usefully treat light as travelling in straight lines through lenses, although we know that it has wave properties which must be considered when optical resolution is in question. In the simple kinetic theory of gases—say for working out the action of high-vacuum pumps—we can safely treat atoms as small elastic particles and neglect their structure. The essential is to know which aspect is the dominating one in the problem concerned.

If the question of 'black body radiation', which led to the quantum theory, were the only place where the need for it was felt, then the quantum theory might be kept in the background, and only trotted out on special occasions. There is, however, a whole series of important observations in different parts of physics that seem to demand the quantum theory naturally. Take, first of all, the photoelectric effect. We have seen that, when light or any radiation of short wave-length falls on a metal, electrons are shot off, the *number* depending on the strength of the light, but the *speed*, or more correctly the energy, on the kind of light. If the radiation is done up in packets of energy, and this energy can be expended in pushing out electrons, then clearly we should expect each atom of light either to throw out an electron with a definite speed, or to do nothing, but not to throw out an electron with some greater speed. According to the quantum theory, a short wave-length—that is, a high-frequency—radiation should therefore throw out electrons with an energy of motion greater than that which characterizes electrons ejected by radiation of long wave-length.

This is just what is observed: red light does not eject electrons at all from most metals, violet light drives them out with a small speed, ultra-violet light produces greater speed, and X-rays throw out very fast electrons. Red light, the quanta of which are very small, on account of its low frequency, has no effect, because a certain minimum energy is required just to jerk an electron out of an atom: the energy of the red quanta is, for most metals, less than this minimum. Allowing for the small energy required just to free the electron, the energy which the electron acquires can be shown experimentally to be exactly proportional to the frequency of the radiation. This is now so well established that, in cases where it is difficult to measure the frequency of very short ultra-violet waves by ordinary means, the energy of the electrons which they eject from matter has been determined, and taken as a measure of the wave-length. The same method has been applied to the exceedingly high-frequency gamma rays of radium.

A remarkable quantum effect, which strikingly illustrates the particle or packet nature of radiation, was discovered by A. H. Compton. When X-rays fall upon a body those scattered are softer, i.e. less penetrating, than those of the original beam, which means that they have longer wave-length and lower frequency. This in turn means that the scattered quanta have less energy than the quanta of the original beam. Now if we can consider the quantum as a particle, then when it strikes an electron, which is another particle, it will be turned aside, giving up part of its energy to the electron, the sharing of the energy depending upon the angle through which it is deviated, as is simply illustrated by what occurs when one billiard ball strikes another. The small change in wave-length of the radiation scattered is found to vary with the angle through which the rays are turned aside in exactly the way that would be anticipated from the theory which treats both the X-ray quantum and the electron as particles.

Further, photographs of ray-tracks taken with the Wilson cloud chamber have shown the path of the electron knocked on by the ray, and the direction and energy agree with this theory of the impact. The Compton effect, which cannot be explained on any purely wave theory, illustrates in a very straightforward way the particle nature of electromagnetic radiation. So much can the quantum of radiation be considered a particle that, as has been said, it is often called a photon.

The quantum theory is concerned not only in questions of radiation but in any atomic process that has periodic properties, or, in other words, that repeats itself with a frequency of so many times a second. The spinning of an atom or molecule round an axis, like a top, is such a property. According to the quantum theory, a spinning particle can only revolve at certain speeds, and, in particular, cannot revolve very slowly—it can either not spin at all, or must spin at the first permitted speed; just as, if all we demanded of a clock was that it should show twelve o'clock at midday, it might either be stopped, or the hour hand might revolve once, twice, three times, or any whole number of times in twenty-four hours, but not at any intermediate speed.

The consequence of this extraordinary restrictive law is that, if we have a gas at low temperature, where the molecules collide with one another comparatively gently, it is only occasionally that one will spin at all, the blows generally experienced not being sufficient to give a molecule the slowest spin permitted. It follows that, to raise the temperature of the gas at these low temperatures, we do not have to give much more than the energy required to make the molecules rush about more vigorously. At higher temperatures, however, where the motion is more vigorous, the collisions are sufficiently vigorous to spin most of the molecules at the least rate allowed by the quantum theory, and in consequence we have to supply energy, not only to make the molecules hustle along their paths, but also to spin them. This would indicate that it requires less heat to raise the temperature of a gas one degree if it is very cold than to raise it by the same step of temperature if it is hot. This is, in fact, what we find by experiment to be the case.

This effect is even more pronounced with solid bodies, where we are not concerned with free atoms. The result of two different methods of calculation which apply the quantum theory to the vibrations of a solid is the same, namely, that to warm a body when it is exceedingly cold requires next to no heat compared to that required to raise its temperature by the same amount when it is hot. This is in accordance with the striking experiments mentioned in Chapter II, which have shown that, in actual fact, the quantity of heat which raises a pound of copper, say, by 1° when the copper is at ordinary room temperature, will raise the same pound of copper by more than 20° if we start at 250° C below the melting-point of ice. The agreement between observed fact and the predictions of the quantum theory is very close when the consequences of the theory are worked out in detail.

In gases the molecules spin round and round as well as rush hither and thither: further, they can vibrate, the atoms of which they are composed being movable with respect to one another, so that they have periods of oscillation which can be compared to those of a body made up of small masses held together by springs. Electrons within the atom can also vibrate. The vibrations of the molecules manifest themselves not only in the behaviour of gases responding to heat, where impacts of one molecule on another are in question, but also in the response of all bodies, solids, liquids, and gases, to light. They are made evident, for instance, in the effect discovered by C. V. Raman, that the monochromatic light scattered sideways by a transparent substance contains radiations of longer wave-length—smaller frequency and consequently smaller quanta of energy—than that of the main beam. The energy differences between the original and the scattered quanta correspond to molecular vibrations and rotations and the Raman effect can consequently be used to investigate those vibrations and rotations, and so to give evidence about the structure of the molecule. The differences between the effect in the gaseous, liquid, and solid state of the same substance can clearly be made to provide information about the electrical forces binding the molecules together in the condensed (that is, solid and liquid) state. The Compton and the Raman effects illustrate different aspects of the way in which the scattering of radiation involves and confirms the quantum theory.

The spins, or oscillations, of ordinary visible bodies—tops and fly-wheels and projectiles—are, however, not affected by the quantum theory, since the behaviour of the single atoms is not here in question, any more than the atomic theory appears in the weight of such bodies. The weight can only vary in steps, since we cannot have any smaller weight than that of one atom, but these steps are very much too small to be noticeable when we are dealing with bodies composed of millions of millions of millions of millions of atoms, and we appear to be able to change our weight at will in a continuous manner. In the same way, quantum spins are very much too small to make themselves felt in any engineering problems, or they would have been detected long ago.

The quantum theory is typical of modern physics, in that it is a case where a special mechanics, unlike that of visible and tangible bodies, is applied to atomic processes. In the physics of the past century, now known as 'classical physics', atoms were always treated as minute bodies, miniature billiard balls, obeying the ordinary laws of mechanics which have been found to govern the behaviour of objects of ordinary size—or macroscopic objects, as they are often called —in contrast to microscopic, or sub-microscopic, objects. Radiations were supposed to be waves in a special subtle medium, the ether, it is true, but their properties were deduced by analogies drawn from the behaviour of such waves and vibrations as can be actually seen or detected in real media, such as air, or water, or solids.

To-day, the results of our experiments have forced us to the conclusion that the laws of motion of atoms and of their parts, and the rules governing the radiations which they send out and absorb, are in many respects of a special kind which can only be found out by trial and repeated comparison with the phenomena themselves. There never was, after all, any reason to suppose that the behaviour of the parts of an atom should obey the same rules of mechanics as the parts of a machine, or as the parts of a solar system, any more than there is any warrant for supposing that the psychology of a crowd reflects that of the individuals composing the crowd. It must, of course, ultimately be possible to work out the behaviour of matter in bulk from the behaviour of the individual atoms, once we know their laws; and of radiation in bulk from the properties of the packets, or quanta, of radiation, although we have found that the reverse—the deduction of the behaviour of the tiny units from that of the bulk—is not possible. At present, however, it is simplest to remember that matter in weighable lumps, and radiations as ordinarily detected, obey the 'classical' laws of mechanics, electricity, and optics, while, for processes concerning single atoms and their little parcels of radiation, special laws hold, of which the quantum theory embodies some of the most important.

Experiment has, then, clearly shown that light, and electromagnetic waves in general, have particle properties. The converse, that ultimate particles have a wave nature, has been strikingly demonstrated by experiments on the interaction of electrons and crystals. In Chapter IV it was explained that crystals offer a very fine and regular structure, by means of which the wave nature of X-rays was established and their wave-lengths measured. Now in 1927 Davisson and Germer found that electrons fired in a beam at a crystal surface, and then turned back, produced not a spot, or a diffuse patch, but a regular pattern, as if especially strong reflexion took place at certain angles. This is just what happens when X-rays are reflected at a crystal surface and can only be explained by their wave properties. The wave-length which had to be attributed to the electrons to explain the pattern obtained was inversely as the velocity of the electron, just as it should be on the theory of wave-mechanics.

At about the same time George Thomson, son of J. J. Thomson, showed that electrons passing through very thin crystalline sheets, in particular metal films so thin that they were transparent to ordinary light, gave rise to beautiful systems of rings closely resembling those produced by the passage of an X-ray beam through a crystal powder or a polycrystalline metal sheet. In the metal film and the powder and the ordinary metal sheet little crystals exist with their axes in all directions, so that the ray always finds plenty set at just the right angle for reflexion. Once more, the wave-length required to account for the size of the rings in the electron case was precisely that given by the theory of wave mechanics for electrons of the particular speed in question.

The wave nature of the electron is now a commonplace of physics and has found very important applications in the so-called electron microscope. The amount of detail that can be seen by an ordinary optical microscope is limited by the wave structure of the light, for when it comes to distinguishing between very close spots of the object, if the distance apart is much less than the wave-length of the illuminating light, diffraction effects come in which cause confusion, thus limiting the magnification that can be profitably used. The resolving power, as the ability to distinguish between closely adjacent points is called, increases as the wave-length used becomes smaller, just as, if a blind man were feeling with a rod differences of structure in a sculptured surface, the finer the point of the rod the smaller would be the details that he could distinguish.

For this reason microscopy with ultra-violet light, which is of shorter wave-length than visible light, was developed, photographic plates being used to record the invisible radiation. But with electrons we can get equivalent wave-lengths much smaller than that of the ultra-violet: thus with electrons speeded up by 10,000 volts the equivalent wave-length is about a fifty-thousandth part of that of visible yellow light, and with 100,000 volt electrons it is less than a third of this. We cannot, of course, use ordinary glass lenses for electrons, for they would neither penetrate the glass to a sufficient depth nor be suitably refracted if they did. We know, however, that electrons are deflected in a magnetic field, the deflection depending upon the strength of the field. With great ingenuity arrangements of circuits have been designed which, when suitable currents pass through them, produce magnetic fields varying from point to point in just the way required. These arrangements constitute the so-called 'magnetic lenses' which focus the electron beams.

An electron microscope, then, consists of an apparatus for producing a beam of electrons of a given energy—that is, a given speed, certain magnetic electron 'lenses', a holder for the specimen, and a fluorescent screen for observation which can be replaced by a photographic plate when permanent record is required. The whole has to be in a very high vacuum to give the electrons free run.

The preparation of the specimen, which must be very thin, is a delicate matter. It may be supported on a fine gauze or on a film of collodion. In the case of solid surfaces, thin films, of plastic substance, can be deposited and afterwards peeled off, acting as casts of details of the surface irregularities. Then these films can be examined by the electron microscope. Very elaborate techniques have been worked out for giving the best results, according to the nature of the object, including the so-called shadowing process with a stream of metal vapour. The limiting factor of the magnification is not, in practice, the wave-length, but the precision of the electron lens: however, whereas about 3000 times is the limit of useful magnification with an ultra-violet microscope, magnifications ten times as great are commonly used in the electron microscope and can be easily exceeded.

The wave nature of other particles, in particular of the proton, of the helium nucleus or alpha particle, and of the neutron, has likewise been demonstrated by experiments on diffraction by crystals. The neutron (see Chapter VIII) has been the subject of extensive experiments because of its great penetrating power and because it is relatively easy to produce, with the modern particle accelerators, beams of neutrons of fixed velocity which, on the theory of wave-mechanics, corresponds to fixed wave-length. A velocity commonly used is equivalent to a wave-length about the same as that of penetrating X-rays.

These examples have been introduced to show how firmly established is the wave nature of the electron and other particles. Returning to light and related radiations, the quantum theory has rendered great services in the field of optical spectra. A heated solid gives out radiations of all wavelengths within a very wide band, as we have considered when speaking of black body radiation. The atoms, and the molecules built up of them, are packed very close, so that their electric fields disturb one another and smudge the sharp outlines of their electronic behaviour. But in gases the atoms or molecules are very sparse, and only come into close proximity for a relatively small part of the time. In gases, then, we have a chance of seeing how isolated atoms behave in giving out and absorbing radiation.

When a gas or a vapour is heated sufficiently, or disturbed by electrons or traversed by a suitable radiation, it gives out light, visible or invisible. For instance, if a metal salt is put in a colourless gas flame it produces a bright light: a sodium salt gives a characteristic yellow colour, a lithium salt a red colour. A gas in a discharge tube, such as the neon in the familiar lamps, likewise gives a characteristic glow. Now the light given out by the atoms of a gas, however they are provoked to emission, is shown by the spectroscope to consist of certain selected wave-lengths only. The spectroscope or spectrograph, in which the light from a slit is analysed by a prism or diffraction grating, shows a series of spectral lines, the position of each one of which gives the wave-length of the light producing it. The light from a hot solid, of course, gives with the spectroscope a continuous band, extending in unbroken range from the red to the violet.

The question is, why does an atom, provoked to give out radiation, emit series of characteristic wave-lengths and not a continuous band of wave-lengths? An atom, as explained in the next chapter, consists of a small positively charged nucleus surrounded, in general, by a cloud of electrons. Moving electrons give rise to electromagnetic waves and the first conclusion is that the light is due to a disturbance of the electrons which make up the outside part of the atom. The simplest atom is the hydrogen atom, with a nucleus carrying one unit of positive charge and, correspondingly, a single electron and, for the purpose of considering light emission, we may take this case.

On the older view, which prevailed before the quantum theory of spectra came in, the electron went round in an orbit with a certain frequency of revolution and radiated light of just that frequency. This, however, meant that the moving electron must all the time be losing energy in the form of radiation and must consequently revolve more and more slowly as time went on, with a corresponding diminution in the frequency of the light sent out. The trouble was, then, that on the old theory the hydrogen atom ought to give a continuous range of wave-lengths—which it did not.

It was Niels Bohr who first made the great advance of saying that the motion of the electron must be governed by quantum laws and not by the laws that govern the movements of planets in the solar system. Whereas on the earlier scheme the electron might have any orbit, Bohr postulated that only certain orbits were possible, orbits in which the electron had a momentum governed by a certain quantum law. Admittedly a large moving charge of electricity radiates, but, in the way generally characteristic of modern atomic theory, it was denied that an ultimate particle of electricity, an electron, moving in the atom, obeyed these bulk laws. In a quantum orbit, it was postulated, the electron continued to go round and round without radiating, although a large charge oscillating in an aerial did radiate.

To each orbit of the group of permitted possible orbits corresponded a certain amount of energy of the electron. Radiation was assumed to take place when one orbit was, somehow or other, replaced by another orbit with a different energy. The frequency of vibration of the light given out was fixed by the simple quantum rule that this frequency, multiplied by Planck's constant, was equal to the differences of energy of the atom in the different quantum states concerned.

There was no inherent reason for the revolutionary assumptions: (1) that the electronic structure of the atoms could exist in certain states only, each determined by quantum conditions of momentum and characterized by a particular energy; and (2) that radiation, of frequency given by a quantum rule, was given out when the disposition, and so the energy, of the atom changed from one permitted state to another. The assumptions were accepted because they produced quantitative results which agreed astonishingly closely with the results of observation, and this is the ultimate test in physics for the validity of assumptions. The quantum scheme accounted for the laws connecting the frequencies of the different lines of the hydrogen spectrum and for certain very small differences between a certain spectral series in helium and one in hydrogen. It could also give an account of the somewhat complicated effect of a magnetic field, or of an electric field, on the light given out by atoms in that field. To account for certain fine details of spectral structure two kinds of quantum number were found to be necessary, one characterizing the general class of the orbit and the other distinguishing orbits, of somewhat different energy, within the class.

When we come to consider more complicated atoms, the grouping of the electrons discussed in the next chapter has to be taken into account. There it is explained how the electrons form certain closed groups, with, in the general atom, an incomplete outside group. Generally speaking, it is the behaviour of the outside electrons that is responsible for the optical spectra. The spectra of atoms with several outside electrons are very involved, but quantum rules which give an account of them have been worked out. These involve three different quantum numbers to determine an orbit, corresponding to the three dimensions of space and, in addition, one quantum number corresponding to the spin of the electron on its own axis, an essential conception introduced by Uhlenbeck and Goudsmit. The electron can only spin with one fixed quantum amount of energy, but in a given atom it may spin about its axis in one direction or the other, clockwise or counter-clockwise, with regard to other electrons. The quantum rules are complicated, but the facts that they have to explain are complicated. The exact position of each line has to be given by the quantum formulae.

The spectra given by an atom possessing all its electrons are not the only ones that have to be explained. An atom which has lost an electron naturally behaves differently, since the electric forces on the remaining outside electrons are changed by the loss. We therefore have to deal with spectra due to an atom short of one electron, due to an atom short of two electrons, and so on. The electrons get knocked off in violent electric discharges. Such spectra too have been classified.

Molecules give a different type of spectrum altogether. Their spectra consist of a multitude of lines arranged in groups which produce an appearance of shaded bands, whence the term 'band spectra' is applied to them. All that can be said here is that some of these complicated band spectra, given out by molecules consisting of two atoms, have been disentangled by the aid of the quantum theory, applied to rotations of the molecule and vibrations of the atoms with respect to one another, as well as to the electronic disturbances, a fairly involved problem.

The essence of the quantum theory of spectra is, then, that by considering a finite number of energy states of the atom, each characterized by a few whole numbers,[1] and by applying the quantum rule connecting energy differences and frequency of radiation, together with rules forbidding certain transitions, we can account for the observed often very complicated regularities. On the old quantum theory the quantum numbers were connected with certain permitted electron orbits. On the newer theory, the theory of wave mechanics, a different interpretation is put on the quantum numbers. Once more, we consider, to begin with, the simple hydrogen atom, with a nucleus of unit charge and a single electron.

Bohr's orbital theory was a wonderful achievement and gave very successful quantitative rules, but the assumptions that he had to make, for instance that of stationary, nonradiating orbits, were admittedly not well warranted by logical considerations. In particular there is a very important fundamental objection to electron orbits. They had never been observed: this alone, however, would not be decisive, for it might always be argued that any day some method might be found to reveal them, as the Wilson cloud chamber revealed the paths of swift particles. But not only had they not been observed: as Heisenberg showed, they were essentially unobservable, for the following reasons.

In order to observe a body it is necessary to get some kind of a signal from it: for instance, we observe a star by virtue of the light which it sends out. If the body will not send out a signal by itself, then it must be illuminated. We can follow the movement of any one of the planets, which are not luminous, because the sun illuminates it for

[1] Half integers also occur.

us. To see the movement of a bat circling in a dark cellar we should shine a visible light on it: to detect the position of a distant aeroplane by radar we send out a beam, not of light but of a different kind of electromagnetic rays, and make observations on those reflected from it. Obviously, then, to detect the position of the circling electron in the atom we must send out a beam of some exceedingly short waves and make our measurements on the reflected beam by some kind of photographic plate or electrical detector. They must be exceedingly short waves, because the shorter the wave the more exact the image formed, and so the better our determination of the position of the electron. It all sounds perfectly simple if only our technique were sufficiently developed.

However, the Compton effect, already described, now comes in and destroys our foundations. The illuminating quantum of radiation behaves as a particle and, when it falls on the electron, knocks it on or knocks it sideways, as one billiard ball does when it strikes another. The higher the frequency—that is, the shorter the wave-length—the bigger the energy of the quantum, and the more serious the push that the electron gets. The act of illuminating the particle, to find out where it is, changes the motion of the electron in a way that we cannot allow for.

It might be suggested that we should use a low-frequency radiation, which implies a small quantum of energy, but that means a large wave-length and, necessarily, a diffuse and ill-defined image, as pointed out when the electron microscope was discussed. So we have the paradox that if the illuminating radiation has a low frequency we give the electron a very small push by the quantum of radiation, but get a very indefinite idea of where it is: if we use a high frequency we get a good instantaneous location, but give it a heavy push which changes its momentum in an unpredictable way. We cannot, therefore, in the essence of things, ever by any conceivable experiment find out at the same time where an electron is and how fast it is moving—if we know where it is precisely, we are very indefinite about the speed, and if we know precisely what is its speed, we are very indefinite about where it is.

It has been proved that, inevitably, the same kind of thing happens with other physical quantities—if we take steps to measure the energy of an electron precisely, we cannot find accurately the instant at which it had this energy, and if we find the instant precisely, we do not quite know the energy. It is this essential, inevitable uncertainty that is embodied in the uncertainty principle first put forward clearly by Heisenberg and known by his name.

The principle tells us about the size of the error that we must perforce make about one quantity, say the position, if we determine accurately its complementary quantity, in this case the momentum. The two errors multiplied together give a product of about the size of Planck's constant, so that if one is large, the other is correspondingly small. Further, the product is so small that neither error is appreciable unless we are dealing with electrons or other ultimate particles.

The act of observing inevitably alters the event when ultimates are concerned—that is the essence of the matter. An example from ordinary life may illustrate the position. It is impossible for a headmaster to find out by direct observation how the boys behave normally, because the mere fact of his coming to look makes them behave abnormally.

This principle has fundamental implications concerning the boundaries of knowledge, which are discussed in the final chapter. At the moment we are concerned with the fact that it emphasized certain difficulties inherent in the orbital picture, clear and useful as it is. The orbital scheme suffered under the logical difficulty that the size of the orbit, and the behaviour of the electron, were fixed by the classical laws of mechanics and of electrical attraction, just as if it were a planet in a very minute solar system with electrical attraction instead of gravitational attraction, but the classical laws were denied when we came to radiation properties. The uncertainty principle introduced another logical difficulty into the orbital scheme.

Louis de Broglie was the first to replace the electron in the hydrogen atom by a wave system, the characteristic wave-length of which was determined by the quantum considerations involving the momentum of the electron, just as in the old theory the energy was connected with the frequency by quantum considerations. The wave system had no definite position, of course, but a certain maximum disturbance was associated with the electron by mathematical laws. The theory was speedily developed and modified by, in particular, Schrödinger and Born. Schrödinger worked out a mathematical system of waves which described the behaviour of particles, but it was Born who gave an interpretation which can be described in a simple way.

The mathematical equations which give the behaviour of the electron in the hydrogen atom are of the kind that describe stationary vibrations. The simplest and most familiar type of such vibration are those of a violin string, fixed at both ends but able to vibrate in a number of different ways, each corresponding to a given note, according to the number of vibrating segments into which it divides itself. A string has one dimension. A plate fixed at the centre, or a membrane like a drum head, which are two dimensional systems, are clearly more complicated vibrators, because, roughly speaking, the surface can divide itself into patches of complicated shape. A vibrating space, in three dimensions, is more complicated still, because it can be going to and fro, concertina-wise, in a great variety of ways, different surfaces considered in it behaving in different ways, and different points on the surface behaving in different ways. The mathematics used in wave mechanics corresponds to the steady modes of vibration of the space inhabited by electrons, steady in the sense that at any particular point the vibration repeats itself over and over again, in time with that at near points of the same part of the wave pattern.

This is the kind of interpretation that the wave equations can bear, but it is not supposed that anything material is vibrating in this way. However, what is essential, and easily understood, is that the calculations indicate a number of ways in which steady vibrations can take place, a number of stationary states. This clearly corresponds to the number of kinds of possible orbits on the older theory. But whereas the orbits selected as stable had to be chosen from all the mechanically possible orbits by somewhat artificial quantum rules, the equations of wave mechanics furnish the stationary states without any forcing.

What is necessary, in order to explain the line structure of spectra, is energy levels in the atom, that is, a number of particular energy states which are the only possible ones, just as in a theatre there are a number of distinct levels with definite numbers (prices) attached to each and one cannot have a seat at any odd intermediate figure that one cares to name. The system of wave mechanics furnishes the levels, which can be accurately worked out in detail for the simpler atoms, more particularly for the hydrogen and the helium atoms. The energies being known, together with certain rules limiting the kind of transition that can take place from one set of energies to another, the frequencies of the radiations can be worked out by simple quantum considerations, just as in the older theory.

Do the actual vibrating patterns, then, correspond to nothing? It has been shown that they can be interpreted in quite a simple way. Something corresponding to the energy of vibration at a particular spot measures the probability that an electron shall be at that spot. A long way from the nucleus this energy figure is vanishingly small, which means that it is most unlikely that an electron will be found there, and there are certain regions near the nucleus where the probability is likewise zero, regions which electrons do not visit. Eddington summed up the matter with his usual graphic power when he referred to the electron, on the new theory, being a sort of probability haze all over the atom.

We have an electron cloud, something like a cloud of circulating gnats. A child, corresponding to the nucleus, is surrounded by a swarm of gnats. It is impossible to lay down a rule as to where a single gnat shall be at any particular moment, but it should be possible to find rules showing exactly how much more probable it is to find a gnat near a bare neck than near a well-protected middle. In imagination one might have a rule that would give, say, the exact odds to lay that a gnat would be found in a space the size of a pea six inches horizontally from an ear. Alternatively, which would come to the same thing, an artist might draw a picture showing no individual gnat, but indicating, by shading, a cloud dense in gnat-frequented neighbourhoods and very thin where gnats seldom came.

The wave mechanical method gives the odds that an electron will be in any particular small region at any time: the orbit picture gave the exact position of an electron at any instant. The greater indefiniteness corresponds to the uncertainty of the uncertainty principle—a precise probability, but no precise event.

The so-called optical spectra cover the radiations, of discrete frequency, which atoms and molecules can be provoked to send out, not only in the visible region but also in the ultra-violet and infra-red regions. Atoms, however, also send out X-ray radiations, but to excite these more violent methods are necessary. Electrons with a velocity corresponding to a few volts suffice to stir up an atom to emit visible light, but to excite X-rays as normally used tens of thousands of volts are required. This is to be expected, for, on the quantum theory, a frequency 10,000 times as great means an energy transaction 10,000 times as great. Correspondingly, the electron groups concerned are those in the interior of the atom, closer to the nucleus and bound with greater energies. The change of energy in passing from one stable system to another is large when such electrons are concerned. Certain basic facts concerning X-rays are at once explained by these simple considerations. To get penetrating X-rays, which means very high frequencies, we have to use atoms of high nuclear charge as the target in the X-ray tube: the high charge means inner electrons with high energy of binding. Solids give out X-radiations of distinct frequencies, forming series like optical spectral series, since the inner electrons are not disturbed by the forces at the outsides of the atoms. Such forces, however, disturb the electrons involved in optical spectra, for which reason to get optical line spectra we have to use a gas. Similarly, chemical combination does not affect the X-ray spectra given out by atoms, since only the outside electrons are involved in such combination with other atoms.

Naturally, the study of X-ray spectra has furnished fundamental information about the electron groupings inside the atom. The interpretation of the results obtained involves the quantum theory of radiation and furnishes one of its strongest supports. Whatever kind of atomic or molecular radiation is in question, the quantum theory is supreme. Further, wherever the atomic electrons are concerned, in chemistry, cohesion, and conduction, for instance, it is to the quantum theory that we have recourse in our attempts to disentangle the complicated mass of observations.

The quantum theory is typical of modern science in that it is a case where, when we come to fundamentals, a special system of mechanics has to be invoked. For handling astronomical problems on the largest scale space is now endowed with properties quite different from those of ordinary experience; quite different, in fact, from those with which the astronomers of fifty years ago were satisfied. For them the fundamental principles that served for surveying countries sufficed for surveying the heavens. In the physics of the past century, now known as 'classical physics', atoms were treated as minute bodies obeying the laws of mechanics which have been found to govern the behaviour of objects of ordinary size. To-day it is recognized that atomic happenings cannot be explained on engineering principles.

In a way this general attitude is not, perhaps, as new as it may seem. In early Greek astronomy the apparent motions of the stars were explained by supposing them attached to a sphere, because in the ordinary way bodies are kept at fixed distances from one another by being attached to a surface of some kind. Similarly each planet had its sphere, to which it was attached to account for its movement, and further spheres were introduced to account for departures from circular motion. Something was required to carry the planets round because in the ordinary way of life something is required to carry inanimate moving bodies round. When Newton worked out the mechanics of the heavens he had to introduce gravitational attraction across empty space, for which there was no analogy in ordinary life except, perhaps, magnetic attraction, and that was not in any way understood. Great minds of his time found it impossible to suppose that the enormous pulls in question were transmitted across empty space by an action of which all that one knew was that it obeyed a mathematical formula.

Later, of course, the gravitational attraction of masses was established as an experimental fact in the laboratory, but no such direct verification of its existence was known in Newton's time. The mysterious attraction, which Newton emphatically said that he did not understand ('for the cause of gravity is what I do not pretend to know . . .'), was accepted because it supplied a mathematical scheme which enabled the paths of the planets and of comets, the behaviour of the tides, and so on to be worked out. Gravitational attraction was, in its time, as novel and 'unreal' a scheme, as much a mathematical fiction, as wave mechanics is now.

The mechanism of the microcosm, of the minute world of the atom and still more of the minutest world, the nucleus, is not of the same nature as that of larger objects. This is the fundamental lesson forced home by a vast body of recent experiment. The special behaviour of the sub-world is governed by special sub-world laws, expressed by mathematical equations, the validity of which is an assumption, in the first instance. It was said of the ether of the older physics that it was the subject of the verb 'to undulate' and nothing more. It might be said that the modern atom is the solution of a wave equation and nothing more.

# CHAPTER VIII

## About the Structure of the Atom

Up to the close of the nineteenth century the accepted view was that matter consisted of atoms but that to every element corresponded a different kind of atom, which had nothing in common with the atom of any other element. All atoms were supposed to be unbreakable, indestructible, and of the same nature all through, like a jelly, and not patchy like a currant pudding—homogeneous, as the man of science prefers to say. Clerk Maxwell, the greatest theoretical physicist of his time, called them 'manufactured articles', meaning that once they were made in the beginning they persevered unchipped and unchanged through all time. Explicitly he wrote in 1875: 'The formation of the atom[1] is therefore an event not belonging to that order of nature under which we live. It is an operation of a kind which is not, so far as we are aware, going on on earth or in the sun or the stars, either now or since these bodies began to be formed. It must be referred to the epoch, not of the formation of the earth or of the solar system, but of the establishment of the existing order of nature, and till not only these worlds and systems, but the very order of nature itself is dissolved, we have no reason to expect the occurrence of any operation of a similar kind.' Every statement here is the direct opposite of what is now believed, but Maxwell was a man

[1] Actually he wrote 'of the molecule', but he used the word in the sense in which we now use 'atom'.

of quite exceptional genius, perhaps the greatest physicist of his time. Let this warn us against placing too great a confidence in our scientific beliefs of to-day.

Newton, the supreme figure in the history of science, did, on the other hand, contemplate the possibility of atomic change. 'While the Particles', he wrote, 'continue entire, they may compose Bodies of one and the same Nature and Texture in all Ages: But should they wear away, or break in pieces, the Nature of Things depending on them, would be changed. Water and Earth composed of old worn Particles and Fragments of Particles, would not be of the same Nature and Texture now, with Water and Earth composed of entire Particles, in the Beginning. And therefore, that Nature may be lasting, the Changes of corporeal Things are to be placed only in the various Separations and new Associations and Motions of these permanent Particles; compound Bodies being apt to break, not in the midst of solid Particles, but where those Particles are laid together, and only touch in a few Points.' That is, although ordinary bodies are made of permanent atoms, and break at atomic boundaries, he was willing to suppose that atoms might, exceptionally, be broken and so changed in nature.

Further, we may add, he believed that the transmutation of metals might be possible—and would have grave consequences, saying of a supposed transmutation under discussion, that the way of effecting it 'has been thought fit to be concealed by others that have known it, and therefore, may possibly be an inlet to something more noble, not to be communicated without immense danger to the world'. Immense danger to the world the transmutation of the elements has proved to involve, although, after Newton, no one seems to have suspected it even as a remote possibility, until the present century. Newton was a seer as well as a scientist.

There was little speculation on the matter of atomic structure during the nineteenth century, although it is true that well over a hundred years ago the chemist Prout had suggested that all atoms might be structures built of hydrogen atoms. This supposition had been dismissed because accurate determinations of comparative atomic weights showed that the weights of the different atoms were not a whole number of times the weight of the hydrogen atom—chlorine, for instance, has atomic weight 35.46 and not exactly 35 or 36, as Prout's theory would lead one to suppose, the weight of the hydrogen atom being taken as 1.

The notion that atoms might have parts arose again round about the beginning of the present century, when the existence of the electron had become thoroughly established, for identical electrons can be produced from all kinds of matter, as described in Chapter V, and they are so much lighter than atoms that many of them can be contained in an atom without seriously affecting the weight. The problem remained as to where the positive electricity in the atom could be located, and as to what gave the atom weight, for an atom would have to contain thousands of electrons if these were responsible for its total weight. Lenard clearly showed that electrons could pass through atoms, and that therefore the greatest part of the atom must be empty space. He supposed that each electron in the atomic structure was associated with a positive charge of like size and a certain mass, the little pair being called by him a dynamid. According to him, then, the atom consisted of a number of minute impenetrable dynamids, swimming in empty space and held together somehow in the volume of the atom. This was a great advance, for it associated the mass with the positive charge and insisted that most of the atom was empty. It was, however, Rutherford, some years later, who gave the theory of atomic structure a new form which had the immense advantage that it was sufficiently precise to form a basis for detailed calculation. He was the Copernicus of the atomic system.

Rutherford arrived at the modern conception of the atom as a result of pondering on experiments concerning the passage of alpha particles through very thin sheets of metal. These alpha particles are positively charged atoms of helium which are shot out spontaneously by certain radioactive elements. All the alpha particles from any one kind of element have, roughly speaking, the same velocity, which, in one particular case, is round about ten thousand miles per second, and not very different for other radioactive elements concerned. Such high energies could not be given artificially to atoms by any means at Rutherford's disposal, although, as we shall see later, they are to-day considered insignificant. Nature thus provided a stream of minute atomic projectiles which, in Rutherford's laboratory, were extensively used to test atomic properties.

In particular Geiger, whose name is so widely known to-day on account of the Geiger counter, and, working with him, Marsden, carried out experiments to find how alpha particles, falling in a narrow beam on a thin foil of gold or other metal, were turned aside from their path by the atoms of the metal. If the foil was thin enough, most of the particles went right through, being slightly deflected, more or less, from their original direction, which, on account of their great energy, is what was generally expected by physicists. But—and this is the essential point—it was found that a few were turned aside through a very large angle and that occasionally a particle emerged again on the side by which it went in, even, in rare cases, coming back towards the source. The return was not due to a surface 'reflexion', since, within limits, making the foil thicker increased the number of particles turned back, which showed that the particles must have gone right in.

The slight scatter of the majority of particles going through the foil could be explained as the result of a large number of little deflections, caused by different atoms, but calculation showed that it was out of the question for a switch through a right angle or more to be the result of a number of such little deflections conspiring together.

Now to many, even to experienced workers, it might have seemed a trifle that a very few alpha particles should apparently be turned through a much larger angle than accepted theory would indicate. It might possibly have been an effect to be explained by, say, chance contaminations, not worth following up. One cannot track down everything.

Rutherford, however, saw in it something of supreme importance. It is recorded that he said, much later, of this scattering through large angles, 'It was quite the most incredible event that ever happened to me in my life. It was almost as incredible as if you had fired a 15-inch shell at a piece of tissue paper and it came back and hit you.'

At that time one favoured picture of atomic structure was a sphere of positive electricity the size of the atom, with electrons scattered through it. Such a scheme would allow alpha particles to pass through atoms in the way observed, but could not account for a large enough localized force to turn a swift alpha particle aside by a large angle. Rutherford, having decided that the alpha particle must have been switched round in one event and not as a result of a large number of smaller deflections—as a result of single scattering and not of multiple scattering, to use the physicist's phrase—transformed the theory of the structure of the atom. He saw that a single massive centre of concentrated electric force was necessary. Accordingly he assumed that the positive charge of the atom, and practically the whole mass of the atom, was concentrated in a small space at the centre of the atom, to which a little later the name 'nucleus' was given. The rest of the atom consisted of a bodyguard of electrons, protecting the central core from any but very energetic particles. Referring to this nuclear theory of the atom Eddington wrote, 'In 1911 Rutherford introduced the greatest change in our idea of matter since the time of Democritus'. The alpha particle itself is the nucleus of a helium atom, i.e. a helium atom which has lost its electrons.

The unit magnitude of charge in atomic physics is the charge on the electron. The number of units of positive charge on the nucleus, which in the neutral atom is the same as the number of electrons in the atom, is, as we shall see, something like half the atomic weight of the atom. For instance for silver, of atomic weight 108, it is 47: for gold of atomic weight 197, it is 79. The force between so considerable a charge and the charge on the alpha particle, which is of two units, is very large when the approach is very close. The experiments on scattering indicate that the nucleus is very small, having a diameter only about one ten-thousandth of that of the atom itself, so that the theory of probability indicates that, even when a particle traverses a large number of atoms, anything approaching a head-on collision with a nucleus is rare.

We can get a rough picture of the state of affairs corresponding to a very thin metal foil traversed by alpha particles by imagining a large country, a thousand miles or more across, planted with pine trees six inches in diameter and a mile apart. These trunks correspond to nuclei. A short-sighted bird is supposed to fly in a straight line between the trunks. It only sees a tree really plainly if it gets within a distance of a foot or so, and then it swings aside the more sharply the plainer it sees the tree, that is, the closer it gets before it notices the obstacle. This close approach will not happen very often with trees so sparsely planted. Trees some yards away produce a feeble blurred impression and make the bird deviate slightly, so that in most cases it will fly right across the land and come out the other side in not quite the direction in which it entered, owing to various small jinks. The rare bird which nearly flies into a particular trunk and changes its direction sharply corresponds to the alpha particle switched through a large angle by single scattering.

The original experiments on scattering were carried out by putting in the path of the alpha particles which had passed through the metal foil a little screen of phosphorescent material, actually zinc sulphide: when an alpha particle strikes this material it produces a tiny scintillation of light, which can be observed through a low-power microscope. By this simple scintillation method, which was extensively used in Rutherford's laboratories, the position of arrival is recorded, not the whole path, but this position is sufficient to tell through how big an angle the particle has been turned. The experimental results so obtained agreed well with Rutherford's calculations made on the assumption that atoms contained positively charged cores which violently repelled any alpha particle, itself positively charged, that happened to come near. This agreement sufficed to convince that part of the scientific world that was interested in the scattering of alpha particles of the essential validity of his conception of atomic structure, but a full realization of the importance of this conception came later.

The cloud chamber of C. T. R. Wilson, described in Chapter V, gives us a method of observing the whole path of an alpha particle. Photographs of the tracks of such particles made by Blackett showed that, while most of them are unobservably or only slightly bent, every now and then one is violently turned from its path at a sharp angle, while at this angle another track leads off, so that the path appears to fork into two unequal prongs. One of these prongs is the path of the particle itself, deviated by striking the nucleus of an atom of the gas: the other prong, which is comparatively short if the nucleus is much heavier than the impinging particle, is the track of the nucleus, which is struck so hard a blow that it itself rushes through the gas in a straight line.

The number of distinct forks observed in a given number of tracks, and the angles of the prongs, agree closely with what Rutherford's theory leads us to expect. We can, then, in this way photograph the tracks and collisions of particles so small that a million million of them side by side would only extend over a fraction of an inch, and so light that a million million million of them would not weigh as much as a grain of dust. We detect them by taking advantage of their tell-tale electrical effects.

Before we pass on, let us consider the general picture which we must now form of an atom. At the centre we have a nucleus which, if we magnify it a million million times, will be about the size of a pea. It must not, of course, be thought of as a definite body like a small pea, but rather as a centre of electric force pervading the surrounding space. What we mean by the size is that, when we approach from outside the vague boundary which takes the place of a surface, the force suddenly becomes very great. If we had a very strong fire nobody would approach nearer to it than a certain distance: this would mark out a kind of limit, though there would be no actual wall there. It is somewhat in this sense that we speak of a boundary and a size for the nucleus.

Around this nucleus clusters a swarm of electrons, some on the whole closer, others farther out, the number and arrangement depending on the kind of atom. In the case of the heaviest atoms there are over ninety of them. These electrons occupy a space which, when magnified like the nucleus a million million times, would be about a hundred yards across. They occupy it not as water occupies a tank, for in the case of hydrogen there is but one of them, but in the sense that they patrol it like a guard. They prevent the electron patrol of other atoms from entering, and this patrolled sphere we therefore call the size of an atom, since two atoms brought together by ordinary collisions will bounce off from one another as soon as these loosely occupied spaces touch.

As already explained, on the modern theory known as wave mechanics the electrons have no very definite positions. The mathematical equations that describe them give, rather, the chance that an electron will be found at a particular place. Where on the older theory we should definitely locate an electron at a particular instant, we now say that the chance of finding it there is high. An indefinite electron cloud, then, perhaps gives a better notion of the case as we now conceive it than an electron patrol.

When a very energetic particle, like an alpha particle or a swift electron, encounters an atom it can break right through the electron cloud, which we ordinarily call the atom, experiencing only small deflections. In the ordinary case, the nucleus being so small, the particle will pass right through the atom without much ado, but should it, as happens now and then, pass near the massive and forceful nucleus, it will swerve aside like a raider approaching a powerful fortress. The atom is, then, mostly empty space, and what is not empty space is centres of electric and magnetic force—a very strong and massive centre of force, repelling positive charges, at the centre, with a diffuse field of oppositely directed force, obeying certain quantum grouping laws, in the outer parts.

The number of electrons which make up the outer parts of the atom is fixed by the magnitude of the nuclear charge. The charge on the electron being taken as the unit in all atomic considerations, for every unit of positive charge on the nucleus there is normally one electron in the atomic structure. We say 'normally' because by electric forces electrons can be removed from the atom, easily if it is a question of one or two outer electrons, but with more difficulty if large numbers are in question. In certain stars which are at prodigiously high temperature, notably the Companion of Sirius, the density is quite abnormally high—about 60,000 times that of water or about 3000 times that of platinum, to arrive at which figure convincing observations of the greatest ingenuity and accuracy had to be made. The density of Van Maanen's star is even greater: in Eddington's words, a ton of this stellar matter would easily go into your waistcoat pocket. (He did not add that you would be shrivelled up long before it got anywhere near your waistcoat.) These densities mean that the volume of the atoms has been made abnormally small by boiling off, so to speak, at the very high temperatures practically all the electrons. There is no possibility of doing this to matter in bulk in terrestrial laboratories.

Atoms combined into molecules in any ordinary substance, in, say, salt or washing soda, are, in the ordinary sense, in contact: the separation of their centres is about the diameter of atoms as found from, say, their behaviour in a gas. This means that chemical combination is, generally speaking, an affair involving outside electrons only, outside electrons being shared, or outside electrons being exchanged, between combining atoms, for instance. Now it is a discovery going back nearly a hundred years that as we go up the series of chemical elements, in order of mass, starting with the lightest, hydrogen, then, at certain intervals, we come across elements with very similar chemical properties. Thus the 3rd, 11th, 19th, 37th, and 55th in the series are lithium, sodium, potassium, rubidium, and caesium, which are the soft alkali metals, all resembling one another in chemical and physical behaviour. Again the 2nd, 10th, 18th, 36th, and 54th in the series are helium, neon, argon, krypton, and xenon, which are the so-called rare or noble gases, also named the inert gases because they are unwilling to combine chemically with any other element. So they, again, are chemically alike.

These are just examples, illustrating the arrangement of the elements in periods. There is first a group of two elements, hydrogen and helium, ending with the inert gas helium; then a group of eight, the elements from lithium (3) to neon (10), likewise ending with an inert gas, neon; then another very similar group of eight, from sodium (11) to argon (18); then a group of eighteen, from potassium (19) to krypton (36), beginning and ending with elements similar to those at the beginning and end of the groups of eight, but with a party of elements of new properties inserted in the middle; then another group of eighteen, beginning with rubidium (37) and ending with xenon (54); and then a very complex group, which once more begins with an alkali metal, caesium, and ends with radium emanation, or radon, which behaves as a rare gas. There are some still heavier elements which are all radio-active, or unstable.

This periodicity in chemical and physical properties of the element in bulk finds expression in the modern theory of the structure of the electronic part of the atom, which is founded on the epoch-making work of the Danish physicist Niels Bohr, briefly discussed in the preceding chapter. The characteristic number for chemical, and much physical, behaviour is that denoting the place when the elements are arranged in order, which is the number given in brackets after the elements named above. This is called the atomic number Z; it gives the number of units of positive charge on the nucleus.

We interpret the facts as follows. There is first of all a

nucleus of charge 2, with a complete group of two electrons, representing helium, the group being closed in the sense that it will neither accept an electron from any other atom nor part with an electron to any other atom, nor will it share electrons. This means chemical inertness. If we now consider a nuclear charge 3, lithium, the new electron will start a fresh group, the alkali metal properties being those corresponding to a single electron added to a closed group. As we increase the nuclear charge by steps of 1, adding each time a fresh electron, we build up a fresh group, which is closed and complete when the eighth electron has been added, the complete group once more corresponding to chemical inertness, neon. A new, eleventh, electron will start a new group: we have an atom consisting of closed groups plus one odd electron, corresponding to an alkali metal.

The completion of the second group of eight closes the system with another inert gas, argon, and the nineteenth electron (one closed group of two and two closed groups of eight making eighteen) starts a fresh group with an odd electron: we have an alkali metal again. This group of eighteen atoms which we have now reached is more complicated: electrons break away and form sub-groups, in a way accounted for by the complete theory, and to the sub-groups correspond new chemical properties. For instance, the elements from scandium, 21, to nickel, 28, have properties not found earlier in the series: this group includes the strongly magnetic iron, cobalt and nickel, for instance. But when the whole group of eighteen is being closed we come back to the properties of the elements in the earlier groups of eight, and finally close the group with an inert gas element, krypton. It is a complicated matter to follow the building up of the groups, especially the long group of thirty-two, and even the groups of eight have a substructure which accounts well for the way that the properties of the elements vary through the group. All that it is desired to emphasize here is that the size of the nuclear charge, which is expressed by the atomic number, fixes the number of electrons in the neutral atom, which in its turn fixes the chemical properties, and, further, that the building up of the electron structure which accompanies increase of atomic number shows a periodic recurrence of certain structural features which correspond to the periodic chemical properties expressed in the periodic table of the elements.

Not only the chemical properties but the optical properties of atoms, and of molecules, are governed by the behaviour of the outer electrons, as explained when the quantum theory was under discussion. It is, then, easy to understand that an atom can be identified by its optical spectrum, a fact used both in the spectroscopic survey of the heavens and in the investigations of the chemical laboratory, used in the analysis both of celestial bodies and of terrestrial minutiae. The spectrum of an ionized atom is likewise characteristic of the ionized state. Since what is in question is ordered vibrations, sequences of separate frequencies, it is permissible to say that the spectrum is the signature tune of an atom or molecule.

We have frequently had occasion to speak of the mass of atoms. Before, roughly speaking, the First World War this could only be found by chemical means. In certain compounds two different elements combine in the proportions of one atom of one to one atom of the other, or in some other very simple proportion, so that by weighing in a delicate balance the amounts that actually combine, we can find the relationship of the weight of one kind of atom to the weight of the other kind. Knowing the weight of an atom of one element, say hydrogen, which can be estimated by special methods, glanced at when we were discussing Brownian motion, the weights of all other atoms can be found by studying suitable chemical compounds, and these weights are the so-called atomic weights tabulated in all books on chemistry.

One atom is chosen as standard, namely oxygen, whose mass is taken as exactly 16. One-sixteenth of the mass of the oxygen atom is, then, the unit of atomic mass. It is this that is meant when, in atomic discussion, unit mass is mentioned. The mass of the hydrogen atom comes out to be

1.008 atomic mass units, sometimes written a.m.u.; in grammes it is $1.673 \times 10^{-24}$, which means 1.673 million million million millionths of a gramme. It might seem the obvious thing to take the mass of the hydrogen atom as unity, but there are good reasons for not doing so: they will appear later.

It must be noted, however, that in chemical experiments on combining quantities the amount which we actually weigh consist of millions of millions of millions of millions of atoms, so that what we are really finding is an *average* atomic weight. Of course, if all atoms with the same chemical properties should weigh the same, as was tacitly supposed until early in the century, the average would give us the same results as an individual weighing. If we have two bags, one containing a million nuts and the other a million bolts, weighing the bags will give us the relative weight of a nut and a bolt, supposing all nuts to be of uniform weight and all bolts likewise. If, however, nuts made on different machines should be different in weight, although they all fit the same bolts (which corresponds to chemical combination in our atoms), then all we have found is the *average* weight of a nut in terms of that of a bolt.

Now, one of the most important series of researches performed of recent times is that in which F. W. Aston, following up pioneering experiments of J. J. Thomson, successfully determined the masses of individual atoms. In discussing the electron we have already pointed out that a stream of charged particles in a vacuum tube is equivalent to a current, and is deviated from its course by a magnetic force or by an electric force. The force on one of the particles depends upon the charge on it: the deviation which the force produces depends on the mass and upon the speed with which the particle is moving, just as if a ball is hit across a wind the amount by which it is blown aside will depend upon the mass of the ball and upon its speed (supposing, so as to get the force produced by the wind the same, that the balls are the same size in all cases). A golf ball is clearly less deflected by a cross wind than a table tennis ball, and a fast golf ball less than a slow one.

It is easy to produce a flight of charged atoms in an evacuated tube, either by introducing the kind of atoms required as the trace of gas which remains in the tube, or by putting them as a solid compound on the positive electrode. Using a special arrangement of electric and magnetic forces, which correspond to two different kinds of wind blowing upon our ball, and knowing the charge upon the flying atom, which can be deduced from other considerations, the mass of the atom can be calculated from the amount by which it is swept aside from its original path. This amount can be observed, because, luckily, the flying atoms leave their mark upon a photographic plate. If there are atoms of two different masses present their paths will be separated out, as would the paths of two golf balls of the same size and speed, but different weight, in the wind.

Aston's apparatus was, in a sense, a kind of electromagnetic scales for separating out atoms according to their weights, and dropping them into the appropriate places. By its aid he definitely established an astonishing fact—namely, that the majority of chemical elements do not consist of identical atoms, but of a mixture of atoms which, while having the same chemical properties, have different masses. That this was possible was suspected even before the First World War, in the first place by William Crookes, who, as long ago as 1886, said, 'I conceive, therefore, that when we say the atomic weight of, for instance, calcium is 40, we really express the fact that, while the majority of atoms have an actual atomic weight of 40, there are not a few which are represented by 39 or 41, a less number by 38 or 42, and so on. We are here reminded of Newton's "old worn particles". . . . This may seem an audacious speculation, but I do not think it beyond the power of chemistry to test its feasibility.'

By 1913 there was strong evidence, largely due to a very full chemical investigation of the radioactive elements carried out, at Soddy's suggestion, by Alexander Fleck, that there were elements of different atomic weight having the same chemical properties. In that year Frederick Soddy, who originated the word *isotope,* said, 'Each known element may be a group of [chemically] non-separable elements occupying the same place, the atomic weight not being a real constant, but a mean value, of much less fundamental interest than has hitherto been supposed'. 'The same place' means the same place in the periodic table, constructed, as has been said, on the basis of chemical properties. The Greek *isos* means 'equal' (as in 'isosceles') and *topos* means 'place', so that the word isotope expresses just this identity of chemical properties. These earlier bold generalizations have been quoted because they so exactly express what Aston's work, followed by that of Bainbridge in America, showed to be a fundamental fact of atomic structure.

Thus chlorine, with its atomic weight 35.457, is a mixture of atoms of mass 35 and others of mass 37, but all with nuclear charge 17, and so with the same chemical properties. Other elements contain atoms of many different masses: thus, for example, zinc, of atomic weight 65.38, is a mixture of atoms of mass 64, 66, 68, 67, and 70, in order of relative frequency of occurrence, all of nuclear charge 30; and the rare gas xenon, atomic weight 131.3, has nine isotopes, of mass 132, 129, 131, 134, 136, 130, 128, 126, and 124, all of nuclear charge 54. These are stable isotopes, which do not change with time: besides these there are, as we shall see, certain others which discharge a particle and break down—which decay, as is said. The behaviour of the radioactive elements, which led to change of nuclear charge, was, as has been indicated, one of the great signposts to the existence of isotopes.

One of the most remarkable cases of stable isotopes is provided by hydrogen. As a result of the detailed investigation of certain slight apparent discrepancies in Aston's extremely accurate measurements on oxygen and hydrogen, it was found that there existed an isotope of hydrogen whose mass was twice that of ordinary hydrogen. The actual discovery of the new isotope was made by Urey, Brickwedde, and Murphy at Columbia. In the case of no other element do we have different isotopes whose masses bear so large a ratio to one another: with lithium, for instance, the isotopes have masses 6 and 7. Atoms of heavy hydrogen behave chemically like atoms of ordinary hydrogen, but are twice as heavy. The atoms are called 'deuterons', and heavy hydrogen gas is called 'deuterium'. Ordinary hydrogen gas contains about 1 part in 30,000 of deuterium. Any chemical compound which contains ordinary hydrogen can, in principle, be prepared with heavy hydrogen in its place, since the chemical properties of the two isotopes are the same. As examples of heavy hydrogen compounds we may cite heavy water and heavy benzene.

Since the hydrogen in ordinary water constitutes about one-eighth of the mass of the molecule, the molecule of heavy water weighs about 11 per cent more than the molecule of ordinary water, and the measured density of heavy water is, in fact, 1.107, ordinary water being taken as 1. The physical properties of heavy water, which can be prepared in relatively large quantities by electrolysis of ordinary water, are markedly different from those of ordinary water: the freezing-point, for instance, is 3.82° C and boiling-point 101.4° C. The remarkable rumours current, at the time of its discovery, in the popular press, that heavy water was a very deadly poison, were, however, entirely without foundation. Experimenters have both tasted and swallowed it: they report that it tastes exactly like ordinary water, and has no ill effects.

Deuterons have been extensively used as atomic projectiles to effect atomic transmutations, and have proved particularly fertile in new results, as discussed later. A third isotope of hydrogen, called tritium, of three times the mass of the normal hydrogen atom, has been prepared by atomic bombardment, but is unstable and breaks down radioactively, so that it does not exist in ordinary water.

The discovery of isotopes brings a great simplification into the study of atomic structure, for, as is illustrated by the examples given, when the isotopes themselves are considered, it turns out that all atomic weights are very close to whole numbers of atomic mass units. The fractions which appear when the ordinary chemical elements are investigated occur mainly because these elements are mixtures. It therefore looks as if the heavy part of all atoms of different kinds can be built up of simple particles of one mass—namely, the mass of the hydrogen atom. It might appear, from what has already been said when the unit of atomic mass was defined, that the hydrogen nucleus was just a little too heavy to act as a unit of nuclear structure, but one of the fundamental facts of modern physics, which enters into most nuclear questions, is that mass and energy are equivalent. When hydrogen nuclei are built together in intimate association to form nuclei, they lose a little mass which appears as energy that, as we shall see, is used in the terrible hydrogen bombs. It is possible, therefore, to take hydrogen nuclei as units of nuclear composition, it being remembered that an isolated hydrogen nucleus is of slightly greater mass than, say, one quarter of four such nuclei in close association. The hydrogen nucleus is, then, a particle of, in the sense explained, unit atomic mass and unit positive charge and is so important that it has received a special name. It is called a proton: it is a nuclear building stone.

We now go a step further. If the nucleus consisted of nothing but protons, an atom weighing 35 times as much as a hydrogen atom would have a charge of 35 units, and would hold round it 35 electrons in the body of the atom itself. It is found, however, that the nuclear charge, which can be deduced from scattering experiments and X-ray measurements, is far less than the atomic weight of the atom in question. For instance, both chlorine atoms, of weight 35 and 37 respectively, have a nuclear charge of 17. Apparently, therefore, the nucleus must contain, in addition to protons, particles which have mass, but no charge. Another possibility, at one time accepted, would be that the nucleus contained, in addition to a sufficient number of protons to make up its total mass, a number of electrons which cancelled the charge of some of them without adding appreciably to the mass. There are, however, strong theoretical arguments against the existence of electrons in the nucleus.

There exists a particle which has almost exactly the mass of the proton,[2] but which, unlike the proton, carries no charge. To denote its electrical neutrality it bears the name of neutron. Much work which contributed to the discovery of this particle was done by Bothe and Becker in Germany and by Irene Curie and Joliot in France, but the first clear recognition of its nature, in 1932, was due to Chadwick in Cambridge, who is entitled to rank as its discoverer.

The neutrons originally studied were produced by the impact of alpha particles on certain species of light atom, in particular beryllium, and it was soon made clear that they came from the nucleus. At the time of the early investigations in question the alpha particle was still the standard atomic projectile used for attacks on the nucleus. To-day atomic projectiles produced by the high-energy accelerators discussed in the next chapter are applied to effect nuclear reactions which give much more abundant supplies of neutrons and convincingly prove that the neutron is an essential part of the nuclear structure of all atoms. Since the nucleus is built up of neutrons and protons, the term 'nucleon' is often used to include both particles.

It is in terms of protons and neutrons, then, that the existence of isotopes is explained. The number of protons in a nucleus gives the positive charge and so determines the chemical nature of the atom: the neutrons which it contains each add one unit to the mass, but leave the positive charge unaffected. Isotopes of a given element, then, all contain the same number of protons, but different number of neutrons. The nucleus of the 35 isotopes of chlorine contains 17 protons and 18 neutrons, the 37 isotopes contains 17 protons and 20 neutrons.

If there were no restrictions on the number of neutrons, the number of isotopes might clearly be very large. There must be laws which prevent the number of neutrons, asso-

---

[2] The accepted values are: mass of proton, $1.6725 \times 10^{24}$ gm.; mass of neutron, $1.6748 \times 10^{-24}$ gm.

ciated with a given number of protons, exceeding certain limits, both high and low, but some elements have a large number of isotopes. Mercury, for instance, of nuclear charge 80 and atomic weight 200.61, has nine stable isotopes, of mass ranging from 196 to 204, and tin, of nuclear charge 50 and atomic weight 118.70, has eleven, ranging in mass from 112 to 124.

The neutron, having no charge, has no electrical reactions of the ordinary type with atoms. One consequence of this is that it has extraordinary penetrating power, passing easily through a block of lead one foot thick. Another consequence is the fact that it does not produce ions in its passage and so its path cannot be directly revealed by the Wilson cloud chamber: further, it cannot be directly detected by the Geiger counter or any of the normal methods used for charged particles or ionizing radiations. The presence of neutrons can, however, be indirectly revealed by such methods, because if a swift neutron strikes a nucleus it may communicate to it sufficient energy for it, the struck nucleus, to produce detectable ions. In much the same way the wind cannot be seen by an observer looking out through a window, but its presence and properties, such as its speed, can be detected by the behaviour of particles which it blows along. Or the neutron may enter a nucleus and cause the expulsion of an ionizing particle or a disruption into two ionizing parts.

To break an atom, in the sense of removing part of its structure, is an easy matter if the outside electrons are in question. For instance, electrons such as pass in an ordinary discharge tube or a fluorescent lamp; radiations, in particular X-rays; heat agitation—all severely disturb the electronic structure and, in general, remove an electron or electrons. But atoms so damaged rapidly repair themselves, for as long as the nucleus, with its positive charge, is uninjured it will build up its due electronic bodyguard in normal circumstances. To produce any permanent change in the properties of an atom, that is, to transform its nature, we must tamper with the nucleus. It is a breaking of the nucleus that is meant when there is talk of 'breaking the atom': removing outside electrons is only chipping the atom and such chips can be easily repaired.

The possibilities of atomic transmutation were first realized through the study of natural radioactivity, as a result of researches in which Rutherford was a leader many years before he put forward the nuclear theory. Round about the beginning of the century it was discovered that certain elements, all very heavy, gave out spontaneously radiations which fell into three classes, to which the names alpha, beta, and gamma rays were given, from the first three letters in the Greek alphabet, $\alpha$, $\beta$, $\gamma$. The alpha particles, which have been often mentioned, are charged atoms of helium. The normal helium atom, in the cold unexcited gas, consists of a nucleus with mass 4 and charge 2, with, correspondingly, two electrons in attendance. The alpha particle is the helium nucleus, without electrons, and accordingly has two units of positive charge: it is made up of two protons and two neutrons, closely combined. The beta particles are swift electrons. The gamma radiations are not particles, but waves of an X-ray nature, and have no charge.

Rutherford and Soddy initiated the theory that the radioactive elements were undergoing spontaneous disintegration, giving rise to a series of elements with different chemical properties. These active elements fall into three families, each beginning with an element that, unprovoked, gives out an alpha particle and becomes another element, because, as we know now, the parent nucleus has lost two units of positive charge in losing the particle. The fathers of the families are uranium, actinium, and thorium. These are the three heaviest natural elements and it is, in a way, not surprising that they should be the ones to fall slowly to pieces, the supposition being that heavier and more complex elements would fall to pieces faster and so have disappeared from the earth.[3] Actinium is very scarce. Uranium and

---

[3] Heavier elements have now been artificially manufactured, as described in the next chapter, and do actually disintegrate

thorium are metals which are scarce, but whose ores are handled by the ton. Their radioactive decay proceeds extraordinarily slowly. The half-period—that is, the time taken for half a given weight to transform itself to the next element in the series—is about fourteen thousand million years for thorium and four thousand six hundred million years for uranium, which is something like the age of the earth. It is because of the exceedingly slow decay that there are still quantities left untransformed.

Taking uranium as an example, a uranium atom gives out, in successive steps, 3 alpha particles and 2 beta particles, forming, through a chain of intermediate radioactive elements, radium. The atomic weight of uranium is about 238 and its nuclear charge, or atomic number, 92. From what has been said it should have lost mass $4 \times 3 = 12$ units and charge $2 \times 3 - 2 = 4$ units in becoming radium, which gives mass 226 and nuclear charge 88 for radium, the correct values. Radium slowly transforms itself, by loss of an alpha particle, to the radioactive gas radon, which transforms itself through a chain of changes until we get the socalled radium G, when the breakdown stops. This is not strange, because radium G is an isotope of lead, and lead is a good, normal, stable element. For anyone who would like to check the arithmetic, there are, in the total course of the successive transmutations from uranium to lead, 8 alpha particles and 6 beta particles emitted, which should give mass 206 and nuclear charge 82. The atomic number of lead is 82 and the atomic weight is 207.2, there being several isotopes, of which 206 is one.

The rates at which different radioactive atoms break down differ enormously: whereas the half-period of uranium is the large number of million years already cited, one radioactive element in the uranium series has a half-period of a millionth of a second. Note, as an example of one of the fundamental uncertainties of physics, that it is impossible

---

much more rapidly than the natural radioactive parent elements, uranium, actinium, and thorium.

to say how long it will be before a given selected radio-active atom transforms itself. We have only a statistical law, just as we have with human life. We know that, if we take a million atoms of a given kind, half will have transformed themselves in such and such a time: if we take a million babies we know that such and such a proportion will normally live to be eighty, but of a particular atom or a particular baby we cannot say if it will die forthwith or live long.

Natural radioactivity both showed that atoms could be transformed and furnished Rutherford with his swift atomic projectiles for the investigation of nuclear forces. With alpha particles he produced artificial transmutations of certain light elements, light elements being selected because they have a small nuclear charge, which gives a bigger chance of close approach by a swift positively charged particle. In these early experiments he used the method of scintillation to detect the particles expelled and was able to demonstrate that alpha particles could drive a swift proton out of a nitrogen nucleus. This was strikingly confirmed by Blackett, using the Wilson cloud chamber method. A close impact leading to the expulsion of a proton is a very unusual event, but as a result of taking 23,000 photographs he obtained six clear records of this cataclysm. Two photographs of the cloud tracts were taken from directions at right angles, so that what was happening in three dimensions might be deduced. Since the alpha particle did not appear after the collision and a proton was expelled, it was concluded that the nitrogen nucleus had increased its positive charge by 1 unit and its mass by 3 units, and so had become an isotope of oxygen. An artificial transmutation of the elements had, it was convincingly argued, been produced.

Rutherford and Chadwick, using the alpha particle as disruptor and the phosphorescent screen as detector, were able to demonstrate the expulsion of a proton from nuclei of many other light elements besides nitrogen. Further, in certain cases they proved that the energy of the expelled particle was greater than that of the incident particle, showing that some energy must have been derived from the nucleus itself, the new nuclear configuration having less energy than the original arrangement. These early artificial transformations of light elements were of the greatest scientific significance but what was in question was single atomic events: there was no question by these methods of transforming a weighable, or microscopically visible, quantity of matter. These experiments, carried out during the years 1921 to 1924, represent the glorious end of the reign of the alpha particle and scintillation method, which Rutherford and his school turned to such extraordinary account. The apparatus was of the simplest, could be set on a small table and picked up with ease; the underlying ideas were simple; the results were, in the true sense of the word, epoch-making. But the time was near when alpha particles were to be superseded by artificially produced particles, available in immensely greater numbers and, very soon, of immensely greater individual energy. The serious attack on the nucleus, with all its consequences, was at hand.

## CHAPTER IX

## About the Structure of the Nucleus

THE most startling, in every way, feature of physical research of recent times is the disruption of the nucleus. Some account has been given of the great discoveries effected by Rutherford and his school, using the alpha particle. A tenth of a gram of radium, which is rather more than equivalent to the source which Rutherford used, gives off—in all directions—several thousand million alpha particles per second, with energies that it would require a potential difference of nearly 4 million volts to produce with the doubly charged particles in question. But when it is remembered that the number in a narrow beam in one direction will be but a very small fraction of the total number emitted and that only about one particle in a million makes an effective nuclear hit under typical conditions, then the number does not seem as large. Another indication to the same effect is that the current corresponding to the passage per second of the total number of alpha particles just cited corresponds to about a thousand-millionth of one ampere. Again, 4 million volts sounds a very respectable figure, but we shall see that it is not much by present-day standards of atomic projectile.

The astonishing information about nuclear behaviour which is now to be considered is the result of observations made on the effects of particles of very high energy. There are, broadly speaking, two classes of particle in question in the most recent nuclear work, natural and artificial. Just as the natural alpha particles were the first atomic projectiles to be used and, although in small supply, gave astonishing results in the early stages of nuclear research, so the natural particles of the cosmic rays, although very sparse, far exceed in individual energy anything that we can yet produce artificially and have led to the discovery of certain new particles which are now in the course of being produced artificially.

The attack on the nucleus is the research characteristic of the present generation. Various journals deal mainly with nuclear problems: there is, in fact, a periodical with the attractive name of *Nucleonics*. The great engineering constructions developed for the production of atomic particles of high energy are one of the most astonishing features of modern science, if not of the modern age. Their construction and operation is an undertaking involving the greatest skill in physics, mathematics, and electrical engineering. Vast sums of money are involved and already special books on the subject are appearing, such as R. Stephenson's *Introduction to Nuclear Engineering,* which is but one of a series of books on the topic, dealing with such matters as radiation shielding, reactor materials, and remote handling equipment. It may be reasonably conjectured that more money is being spent and more individuals employed on the construction and running of a single one of the latest such machines than were involved in physical research all over the world at the time when the pioneering work on radioactivity and electron physics was being done. Atomic research has taken on a completely new aspect, as different from that of the classical days of Rutherford's work as is the modern machinery of drama, represented by the constructions of Hollywood, from the Globe playhouse of Shakespeare's time.

It was in 1932 that Cockcroft and Walton produced the first nuclear transmutation by means of artificially accelerated atomic projectiles, as distinct from natural alpha rays. This work convinced the world of physics that the new science of transforming the chemical nature of atoms—nuclear chemistry, if we may so call it—was awaiting development and that the prime need for speedy advance was a copious supply of atomic projectiles of high energy.

The apparatus of Cockcroft and Walton consisted of a more or less standard method of producing, by a high-voltage transformer, a potential difference of 200 kilovolts or so, which, by a novel and very ingenious method of switching, could be multiplied three or four times. Potentials of from 200 kilovolts upwards were used to accelerate protons, obtained from ordinary hydrogen gas, and with these protons it was shown that lithium could be converted into two swift helium nuclei, or alpha particles, which works out correctly, since the nuclear charge of lithium is 3 and the mass of one lithium isotope is 7, so that adding 1 to the mass and 1 to the charge can give two particles, each of mass 4 and charge 2. The number of transmuted particles went up very rapidly with the potential, but the nature of the transmutation was always the same. The method used for detecting the transmutation was the Wilson cloud chamber. The two separate helium nuclei coming from the lithium nucleus could be seen as two long tracks, in exactly opposite directions from a point in the path of the projectile beam and their energies could be calculated from the length of their tracks.

The energies of the individual protons producing the transmutation, even at 800 kilovolts, are low compared to that of natural alpha particles and, as will be seen, the probability of disruption by a single particle decreases rapidly as the energy diminishes. However, the number of particles in Cockcroft and Walton's beam was so enormous compared to that available from practicable radioactive sources that it more than compensated for the lower probability corresponding to the lower particle energy. As well as protons, Cockcroft and Walton used as projectiles deuterons, i.e. nuclei of the heavy isotope of hydrogen, with twice the mass of the proton.

Besides the artificial production of helium from lithium, two most important theoretical points were established by the experiments now in question. The nucleus carries a positive charge which has a repelling action on a positive particle, an action represented by the assumption of a surface of high potential all round the nucleus, termed, for obvious reasons, the potential barrier. A positive particle escaping from within the nucleus will be repelled by this barrier, and the energy of the alpha particle indicates a barrier of some 4 million volts. On the older, now called classical, views this would mean that a particle would have to possess an energy corresponding to a fall of potential of this magnitude if it were to penetrate the nucleus and produce a transformation: any particle with a less energy would be repelled by the barrier, which could be likened to a smooth mountain ring of uniform height, which no one could cross unless he had the energy needed to climb the height. On this view it would not matter how many particles with an energy corresponding to, say, 1 million volts were launched at the nucleus: they would all fail to surmount the barrier.

On the modern theory of wave mechanics, however, everything is a question of probability when it comes to elementary processes. As shown by Gamow, on this theoretical basis the chance of a particle traversing a potential barrier is greater the greater its energy, but has a finite value for energies much below that necessary to transmount it on the old views. It is as if there were various tunnels through the mountain ring, very difficult to find low down, by the man who only had a small fraction of the energy needed to climb to the top and descend, but easier to find higher up, by the man with greater energy, but still not surmounting energy, if we may now call it that. It is, in fact, not unusual to speak of tunnelling through the potential barrier. By producing nuclear disruption with accelerating particles far below that necessary on the classical theory, Cockcroft and Walton proved the validity of the new, wave-mechanical theory of piercing the potential barrier.

The other theoretical result in question is of possibly even greater significance and concerns the relationship between mass and energy which resulted from Einstein's development of the theory of relativity. The older belief was represented by two principles, the conservation of matter and the conservation of energy. By the conservation of matter was meant that, whatever physical or chemical changes took place, matter could be neither destroyed nor created, but only changed in structure and combination. Very delicate experiments were carried out to prove that in chemical reactions, such as when, to take a simple case, two chemical compounds interchanged atoms, no change of total mass took place, and it was shown that, in one particular case, there was no alteration amounting to 1 part in 100,000,000. Similarly, when energy changed its form, from work to heat, as in friction, or from electrical to heat energy, there was no change in the total amount of energy, which was also proved experimentally, although a like precision was not here possible.

Einstein's conclusion was that it should conceivably be possible for mass to be changed into energy, or energy into mass, according to a simple rate of exchange, represented by

$$E = mc^2$$

where $E$ is the energy, measured in ergs[1] if the mass $m$ is measured in grams, and $c$ is the velocity of light, namely 30,000,000,000 centimetres per second. This means that a very small change of mass represents a very large change in energy: the conversion of 1 gram (less than 1/28 of an ounce) would give, according to the formula, energy represented by a million horse-power for 33 hours. The changes of energy that take place in chemical reactions, such as burning or attack by acid, would correspond, then, to mass changes far too small to be detected, which would account for the negative results in the old experiments.[2]

The first definite experimental proof of Einstein's mass-

---

[1] The erg is a very small unit. A foot pound is about 13 million ergs.

[2] The energy produced by burning a given amount of good coal would be equivalent to less than a thousand-millionth of its mass.

energy law was given by Cockcroft and Walton's artificial transmutation of a lithium atom into two alpha particles. The energy of motion of these two swift particles was large —where did it come from? The energy of motion of the proton that, by its impact, produced the change was far too small to supply it. But the mass of the lithium 8 atom is 8.0261 and the mass of the two heliums is 8.0078, in atomic mass units. There is, then, a small loss of mass in the nuclear transformation, and Einstein's formula shows that this is just represented by the energy of motion of the two helium nuclei, allowance being made for the (comparatively small) energy of motion of the proton involved in the change. The important lesson is that nuclear reactions may involve a comparatively large—something not very different from 1 per cent—change in mass, which represents an enormous amount of energy. Hence the atomic bomb and the hope of industrial atomic energy, all represented by an equation that a child can understand.

It is, perhaps, of interest to set down here Isaac Newton's prophetic words of some two hundred and fifty years ago, 'The changing of Bodies into Light, and Light into Bodies, is very conformable to the Course of Nature, which seems delighted with Transmutations'.

Before discussing the astonishing artificially produced nuclear changes which have followed the work of Cockcroft and Walton, it may be well to glance at the methods that have been used to produce the prodigious voltages that are now a commonplace and to say a word about methods in general before considering results. The simplest form of high-voltage machine—and by high voltages we mean those measured in millions and ten millions of volts—is based on the old principle of the frictional machine, extensively used for electrical experiment in the eighteenth and nineteenth centuries, of which improved versions were to be seen at the beginning of the present century in laboratories and in hospitals, where they were used for running X-ray tubes. These machines were made of discs of glass, or ebonite or other insulating substance, rotated on a central axis. Electric charges, produced at the start by an electrified rod or by friction, were carried round and multiplied until the potential reached a high value, the electric energy needed to generate and maintain the voltage being derived from the mechanical energy needed to turn the discs.

The Wimshurst machine, in its improved forms one of the best types, could produce voltages up to 300,000 volts, but only very small currents. These machines were, in general, troublesome to run, especially in damp atmospheres, and, with the development of high-tension transformers, fell out of use. In any case, the voltage was not high enough for atomic purposes.

In 1931, however, Van de Graaff designed a completely new type of influence machine, or electrostatic generator, which has been greatly developed. In his machine electric charges are carried not by a disc, but by an endless moving belt of insulating substance, say of multi-ply rubber fabric, looking something like the belt connecting a workshop machine with an overhead drive. At one pulley electric charges are 'sprayed' on to the belt from a row of points connected to a 10,000-volt set, say: the other pulley of the belt is surrounded by a metal enclosure, to which the charges are transferred. One trouble with all machines whose parts have to be maintained at hundreds of thousands of volts is the loss of charge by leakage through the air, accompanied by a glow due to the discharge. This can be very much diminished by enclosing the whole affair in a gas at high pressure, for just as low pressure favours electric discharge through a gas, high pressure hinders it. Recent Van de Graaff generators are enclosed in strong metal housings which will stand an internal pressure of 400 lbs. per square inch or so, filled with special gases. A particular machine of this kind, for atomic acceleration, will work at up to 12 million volts, but very compact electrostatic belt generators, giving 2 million volts, have been built for generating X-rays of high penetrating power. The 5-million-volt installation at the Massachusetts Institute of Technology is enclosed in a pressure vessel about 6 feet in diameter and 16 feet long, a space which is very small for a contrivance producing such a voltage.

Quite a different principle is that used in the cyclotron type of machine, the successful development of which was originally due to E. O. Lawrence, working in collaboration with M. S. Livingston. This has the great advantage that, paradoxically, it produces particles with energies equivalent to a very high voltage without the use of a very high voltage. The essential feature of all such atomic accelerators is that, by the use of a large magnetic field, the particle is made to go round in a roughly circular path, receiving a voltage kick twice in a complete circuit. The effects of these kicks accumulate until an energy is acquired which is equivalent to a large multiple of the voltage applied in a single act of acceleration. Since it is the circling path of the particle that characterizes these machines, they may be appropriately called 'orbital' or 'cyclic' accelerators.

An intrinsic part of the cyclotron is a flat, circular metal box, cut into two by a gap along a diameter, as shown in Fig. 3. This is arranged in a strong magnetic field, with the direction of the magnetic force at right angles to the flat of the box. Any charged particle moving inside the box parallel to this flat is swung into a circular path if the field is strong enough, just as the path of cathode rays is twisted into the arc of a circle in a magnetic field. With whatever speed the particle is moving it takes the same time to go once round, because the faster it goes, the bigger the circle it describes.

Between the two halves of the box, called 'dees' from their shape, an alternating field is applied, the frequency of which is such that it goes through a complete cycle in the time that the particle takes for a complete circuit. This means that, by the reversal of the field, an accelerating kick as the particle goes into one dee is changed to a kick in the other direction when it comes out of that dee having completed a semicircle, which is just what is required if the additions of energy are to accumulate. The added speed means a path of larger radius, so that the complete track is made up of semicircles of increasing radius, forming a kind of spiral.

Thus in a cyclotron installed in E. O. Lawrence's laboratory shortly before the late war, the diameter of the pole pieces of the great magnet was 5 feet, the peak of the alternating potential applied to the dees was of the order of 100,000 volts, with a frequency of 10 million cycles a second or so. Beams of protons with an energy equivalent to acceleration in a potential drop of nearly 10 million volts were obtained. The cyclotron at Birmingham is very similar in size and operating figures.

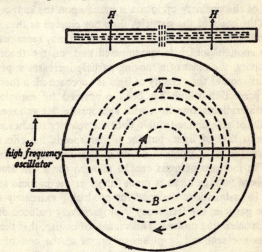

FIG. 3. *The principle of the cyclotron. The spiral path starts at the centre: the beginning and end of the path are not shown. The arrows* H, H *indicate the direction of the magnetic force.* (*As a matter of historic interest the diagram is copied direct from that used by Lawrence and Livingston in their first published description of the cyclotron.*)

Such cyclotrons are, of course, very elaborate and costly installations. To adjust locally so large a magnetic field, to maintain the high vacuum needed in the chamber enclosing the dees, to provide a suitable source of ions, to deflect the beam out of the dee space into the experimental chamber, to keep the beam focussed, and so on, are problems that call for deep knowledge and experience. The magnet weighs a few hundred tons in all. This combination of engineering skill and the physicist's knowledge of the behaviour of ultimate particles is a feature of our age which had no counterpart in the laboratories of the previous generation.

To obtain protons with energies of more than 10 million volts or so means new difficulties to be overcome. The design of the ordinary cyclotron is based upon the supposition that the mass of the particles does not change as they rush round with ever-increasing velocity, which may seem reasonable enough until it is remembered that, on the theory of relativity, the mass of a moving particle increases appreciably as soon as the velocity of light is approached, a theoretical prediction which has been confirmed by experiment. Consideration shows that, with appropriate dee voltage, this need not give undue trouble until the velocity reaches about a tenth that of light, but for higher speeds the effect becomes serious. Cyclotron design is a troublesome affair.

The increase of mass can be allowed for if the interval between voltage kicks is made larger as the particle speeds up. In installations designed for producing extremely energetic particles the frequency is progressively reduced during the accelerating process. This means, of course, that the particles are sent out in pulses or bursts at the end of each cycle of frequency change, but these bursts follow one another very rapidly. The Berkeley synchrocyclotron, as this varying-frequency machine is called, was the first, and is still the largest, of its type in existence. It makes the largest pre-war Berkeley cyclotron look quite small, for the magnet poles are over 15 feet in diameter and the whole magnet weighs 3700 tons, with 300 tons of copper in the windings —a considerable step from the largest electromagnets to be found in laboratories when the properties of the electron and the proton were originally discovered, for they could be moved by a couple of men. The Berkeley synchrocyclotron produces in quantity protons with an energy of 340 million electron volts,[3] about 45 times that of the individual alpha particles with which Rutherford worked. Each particle goes round about 10,000 times in the course of building up the energy, the whole process taking about 1/1000 sec., while there are about 100 of these bursts of fully energized particles per second.

There is still another method of accelerating particles, which operates with a changing magnetic field. The curvature of the path of a charged particle in a steady magnetic field decreases the faster it goes: the curvature of path of a particle of fixed speed increases the stronger the field. Hence if, as the particle goes faster, the magnetic field is made stronger at the appropriate rate, the particle can be kept moving in a circular path instead of the spiral path which it takes in the steady magnetic field of the cyclotron and synchrocyclotron. The changing field can also be made to accelerate the particle by the action of electromagnetic induction. This principle has been applied in what is known as the betatron, the object of which is to produce very energetic electrons, otherwise known as beta particles. The vacuum chamber in which the electrons are speeded up in their circular path is in the form of a flattened ring known, from its shape, as a doughnut, which is fitted with a magnet of special construction. The betatron erected by Kerst and his colleagues at Illinois has produced electrons of energy corresponding to a potential drop of 315 million volts.

The betatron was followed by a new pattern of particle accelerator. It uses a doughnut-shaped vacuum chamber and a magnet producing a rising field to keep the particle in the same path as it speeds up. But the final acceleration is due to a very high frequency (radio frequency) electric field, arranged to operate across a gap so as to give the particle a kick every time it comes round, just as does the field across the gap in the dees in the cyclotron. Full account is taken

[3] 340 is the figure for 1955: it is due to be increased to 730 MeV. (MeV, or Mev, is the symbol for million electron volts.)

of the relativity mass-effect in the design of this prodigious and complicated machine, first proposed by Oliphant when he was at Birmingham, and called a proton synchrotron, because it has some relationship to the synchronous motor. All these orbital accelerations are, in fact, refined applications of electrical engineering.

Three enormous synchrotrons had just been completed at the end of 1954, one at Brookhaven, rejoicing in the special name of *cosmotron* (presumably because it produces particles approaching the energy of the primary cosmic rays), one at Berkeley, called the *bevatron* (from billion[4] electron volts, which is the particle energy that it produces), and one at Birmingham. These machines are the largest yet. In the Birmingham installation, for instance, the magnetic track in which the protons run their race is about 30 feet in diameter, although, on account of its narrow ring form, the magnet weighs only some 800 tons. The original squirt of protons, injected as the magnetic field begins to build up, is from a Cockcroft-Walton generator, at about 450,000 electron volts. In the Brookhaven cyclotron voltages of 3 GeV and more have been reached and the protons *start* with an energy of 4 MeV, obtained by the use of an electrostatic generator of the type already described.

It may be noted, as showing the present-day scale, that one of the great authorities in the subject writes of 'slow particles, e.g. protons of a few hundred MeV or less'! One MeV was a sensation twenty years ago. It appears, however, that 3 GeV is far from the limit and 10 times this voltage is contemplated in machines now being designed, to cost about 20 million dollars. Figures of this kind justify, perhaps, the space devoted to particle accelerators in a small book of this kind. They loom very large when expenditure is considered. In an admirable technical account of cyclic accelerators recently published, Fremlin and Gooden write,

---

[4] In America and in France billion denotes a thousand million, and not a million million as it does in England. The English term for the energy given to an electron by a thousand million volts is giga electron volts, written GeV.

'It is difficult altogether to avoid the suspicion that the first move made by the modern nuclear physicist is to determine, by means which may only in part be scientific, the maximum amount of money which he can reasonably hope to obtain. Once this primary figure is established, attention can be given to the more detailed matters. . . .' This is an aspect of modern physics which cannot be neglected in however slender an introduction to the subject, although possibly it will soon cease to be classed as a branch of physics and recognized as nuclear engineering.

In still another type of particle accelerator cylindrical cavities are arranged in line, all on the same axis, the particles being given a heavy voltage kick on passing from one to the other. This arrangement has the advantage that the problem of getting the beams out of the accelerator, which is a complicated matter in the orbital machines, is here simple. The biggest linear accelerator, as this type of machine is called, for accelerating protons is a 60-MeV machine at the University of Minnesota: there is a bigger one for accelerating electrons at Stanford, which gives electrons of over 200 MeV.

So much for methods of getting particles of prodigious energy, which make the old alpha particles look feeble indeed. Each method has its advantages, involving considerations of number of particles produced as well as individual energies.

When it comes to detecting rays and particles the cloud chamber, so often mentioned, is, in various modifications, a most valuable agent. The special information which can be obtained by putting the chamber into action in a magnetic field has already been mentioned. Blackett and Occhialini further extended its use, in particular for cosmic rays, by making it self-operating. Originally the only way to catch cosmic ray tracks was to keep on repeating the expansions at regular intervals, relying on chance to secure every now and then an informative photograph of particles. Blackett and Occhialini placed Geiger counters above and below the chamber and by ingenious circuits arranged that every ray passing through them both, and so through the chamber, would set off the expansion. Of course the particle or ray will have left the chamber before the expansion has had time to begin, but, as has been pointed out, the atomic debris keeps its station long enough to reveal the tracks in question.

The cloud chamber was used in the recent atomic investigations. The chamber in question was 18 inches in diameter, filled with hydrogen at 8 atmospheres pressure and in a strong magnetic field. A beam of very swift neutrons was shot across it, the neutral particles producing no tracks, since they can produce no electrical effects. When, however, one of them strikes a hydrogen nucleus it drives it on as a rapid proton, which leaves, of course, a track of normal type. Owing to the magnetic field all the proton tracks curve to the left as we follow the path from its start in the neutron beam.

Another type of detector is exemplified by the Geiger counter just mentioned, which consists essentially of a fine wire surrounded by a metal cylinder, enclosed in a small chamber containing a specially chosen gas or gases at a suitable pressure, which is a fraction of the atmosphere. The wire is kept at a potential just not high enough to make a discharge pass. When a high energy particle, or ionizing radiation, enters the chamber it gives rise to electrified atoms or molecules which are driven across by the field, creating in their passage other electrified particles. The result is a minute burst of current, which can be suitably magnified by modern valve techniques, so as either to produce a sharp kick in a photographically recorded track or to operate a mechanical counter. One swift atom, then, can be made by modern methods to turn a small wheel!

A third method which has found most important applications is a direct use of the emulsion of a photographic plate, to be described when cosmic rays are discussed. A fourth is a development of Rutherford's original scintillation method, which consisted of counting with a microscope the individual specks of light produced by particles striking a phosphorescent screen. To-day the light of the scintillations is detected not by eye observation but by photoelectric cells of a particularly sensitive type, called photo-multipliers, with the usual gear of amplifiers, counters, and so on. New scintillating materials are available which are particularly sensitive to penetrating gamma rays. Supposing that the material is transparent to light, we can use a large block surrounded by photo-cells, so that a scintillation will be registered wherever it occurs in the block. Substances used to-day are large transparent crystals of naphthalene and other solid organic compounds, anthracene in particular, and also liquids of certain types. For instance, the largest of the scintillation counters (at the moment) is a tank containing 60 gallons of a sensitive liquid surrounded by 90 photo-multipliers, at Los Alamos. These modern scintillation counters have been used for cosmic rays. Of course with modern techniques any atomic upset produced by particles or quanta can be utilized for counting and the electric conduction of certain 'non-conducting' crystals has been turned to account.

So much for the artificial particles of great energy which are used to-day in nuclear investigations. The methods of detecting nuclear change and disruption effects are the same with these experimental methods as with cosmic ray projectiles, to consider which we now turn.

The realization of the existence of cosmic rays and the investigation of their properties were, as modern physics goes, a matter of comparatively slow development. As long ago as 1900, round about the time when present leaders of cosmic ray research like Blackett, C. F. Powell, and Leprince-Ringuet were born, it was found that air in a closed vessel was feebly ionized, that is, contained a small supply of electrified particles, and if these particles were removed by an electric field, others appeared in due course. It was proved that this small but steady ionization was reduced if the vessel was surrounded by a coating of lead. Hence it was attributed to radiation coming from outside. The natural supposition was that these radiations were gamma rays from traces of radioactive material in the ground, which, indeed, are responsible for most of it. C. T. R. Wilson did suggest that radiation coming from some source outside the earth might play a part, but gave this up when he found that the effect was not reduced in a railway tunnel. It did not occur to anyone at the time that the radiations might be so penetrating that the earth above the tunnel made little difference, since gamma radiation, the most penetrating known, would be completely cut off by so great a barrier.

After certain not entirely conclusive experiments it was finally proved by Hess that an ionizing radiation was coming in from outside. In balloon flights up to 3 miles high he found that the ionization in a closed vessel decreased at first, in a way to be explained by the contribution of terrestrial radioactivity to the effect: above a certain height, however, it showed a systematic increase as the balloon rose. This effect was confirmed by Kolhörster, but the results gave rise to violent controversy among physicists and it may be said that the existence of a cosmic radiation coming in from outside the earth was not universally accepted among physicists until 1926. If this slow progress seems strange, it must be remembered that the effect in question is very small, the production of a few tens of pairs of ions in a cubic inch of air at ordinary pressure every second. To show what this means we may recall that the current through an ordinary small neon lamp corresponds to the removal of something approaching a million million million ions per second from the gas.

The position in 1928 is well summed up by J. J. Thomson and G. P. Thomson, who, about that time, wrote in their *Conduction of Electricity through Gases:* 'At present, however, we do not know nearly enough about these rays to come to any decision as to their nature: it is evident, however, that they raise questions of the greatest interest and importance. It would be one of the romances of science if these obscure and prosaic minute leakages of electricity from well-insulated bodies should be the means by which the most fundamental problems in the evolution of the cosmos had to be investigated.' Prophetic words!

The rays must be very penetrating to get through the atmosphere, which as an obstacle makes up for its low density by its great thickness. It holds up the barometric column of 30 inches or so of mercury, which means that, in weight, it corresponds to a yard thickness of lead, some inches of which completely stop ordinary gamma rays.

The measurements which plainly established the existence of cosmic rays were made with ionization chambers, often filled with gas under pressure, and with very sensitive recording electrometers. In the recent intensive work on the rays the Wilson cloud chamber has played a leading part, especially with the adjuncts of a magnetic field and of a triggering device, already mentioned, by which the ray sets the chamber in operation. It will be remembered that Anderson discovered the positron by investigating the action of cosmic rays on solids in a magnetic field. The cloud chamber in the magnetic field is, then, one powerful standard method. A second method, which in the hands of C. F. Powell and his collaborators has led to most astonishing results and has been very profitably employed by the French and Italian investigators, is the photographic plate.

It may seem strange that the photographic plate, used today for recording results in every branch of physics, should be spoken of as a new method, but what is in question is quite a new application, in which, without lenses or subsidiary apparatus of any kind, the photographic emulsion—that is, the gelatine sheet containing the photographically sensitive grains—is used to record single atomic processes. Once more, as with the cosmic rays themselves, there was a considerable period of mild activity before the power of the method was realized, for as long ago as 1910 observations were made on the effect of single alpha particles on the emulsion, which attracted the favourable comment of Rutherford. It was not, however, until 1935 that an attempt was made, in the United States, to use the emulsion to record the tracks of cosmic rays, by sending plates up to 73,000 feet in a balloon, and a year later Blau and Wambacher actually obtained an indication of some particle effects due to nuclear disintegrations by exposing plates high up in the Alps. By 'exposing' is simply meant leaving them lying about in their wrappings: nothing more is needed. Results of interest to specialists were obtained in the next few years, but up to 1945 nothing at all sensational had been discovered. It is significant that in Millikan's celebrated book *Electrons* (+ *and* −), *Protons, Photons, Neutrons, Mesotrons and Cosmic Rays* (a comprehensive title), published in 1947, where cosmic rays are extensively discussed, the photo-emulsion method is not even mentioned. It may be said, then, that for over thirty years the photographic method of revealing atomic tracks had been to hand, but appeared to be of very modest use. This is a comment on the opinion sometimes expressed to-day that there is nothing simple left to do in physics, that a few thousand pounds' worth of apparatus (or a few hundred thousand pounds' worth, according to the ambitions of the worker) is necessary if anything significant is to be discovered.

The photographic emulsion consists of a very large number of small grains of silver bromide or similar compound distributed in a sheet of gelatine. The action of light, or of swift particles of any kind, is to produce a change in the grain which renders it accessible to the action of the developing liquid, with the familiar consequences. It was a technical change in the manufacture of the emulsion that made it, in the hands of C. F. Powell, so powerful a weapon. The improvement consisted in increasing the quantity of silver bromide and using smaller particles: in the Ilford plates which have proved so successful the amount of bromide is up to 10 times that in normal plates and the average grains are about 1/60,000 of an inch across, say 60 to the thickness of a cigarette paper. The plates have to be examined under high magnification, so that a dense assembly of small particles is needed to define the significant features of the tracks that they reveal. Since, firstly, the tracks may be at any angle with the surface and, secondly, at high magnification only a small part of the track may be recorded on one microphotograph, the complete picture is often a mosaic of separate microphotographs pieced together.

The thickness of the film used for cosmic rays may be about a fiftieth of one inch, which has about the same stopping-power for particles as a yard of air. The alpha particles used so extensively by Rutherford are stopped by 3 inches of air, so that at first the film seems to offer sufficient resistance for particles to complete their tracks in the emulsion. However, certain very energetic particles from nuclear disruptions may have tracks in the emulsion an inch or so long, and even much longer, which would, except for the rare lucky chance of a track parallel to the surface, register but a small part of their path. To deal with these penetrating particles a method has been recently devised of stripping the emulsion from the glass of the plate and making packs of, say, fifty films with no backing, separated by tissue paper. After exposure each film is developed separately and yields its contribution to the history of the path.

Since the cosmic rays are absorbed in the atmosphere it is most valuable to make experiments at high altitudes and the photographic method, on account of its simplicity, lends itself to such work. Special balloons, made of polythene, a transparent plastic material which is impervious to gases and not affected, as is rubber, by intense sunlight, are used. At the great heights reached, 100,000 feet or so, the pressure is only about a hundredth of an atmosphere, which, allowing for the cold, means that hydrogen free to expand will occupy about 80 times the space that it does at the earth's surface and that the lifting power of a balloon of given volume will only be a correspondingly small fraction of what it is at low altitudes, since the air displaced is so much lighter.

These cosmic ray balloons are therefore of peculiar construction, shaped like a sausage about 120 feet long and half that in diameter, with, to start with, a little hydrogen at the top, which expands and inflates the balloon as it rises. Their slack and trailing form looks strange on their upward journey and has, no doubt, given rise to some of the stories of visitors from other planets. They make more or less level flights at the greatest height reached and so expose the plates which they carry for many hours to the high-altitude radiation. The recording equipment is ultimately detached by means of a clockwork mechanism and descends by parachute, usually far from the point of launching. The balloon is lost. At lesser heights records have been obtained by exposing plates for weeks on high mountain stations. Records have even been obtained with the magnetic cloud chamber flown at heights of about 30,000 feet in an aeroplane. The outfit weighed about 2 tons, which contrasts with the total load of 40 lbs. or so carried by Powell's balloons.

Supplementary to the experiments at heights are those which have been carried out underground, in mines and tunnels, and under water in lakes. At 100,000 feet up the total weight of matter (i.e. atmosphere) between the recorder and outer space is equivalent to a sheet of water 4 inches thick; in some of the underground experiments the layer of earth overhead was equivalent to 1500 yards of water, through which, nevertheless, some cosmic rays arrived. This extreme penetration indicates that particles must be present with energy equivalent to many thousands of millions of volts.

In its simplicity and in the importance of the results that it has produced the photographic method reminds us of the scintillation method—alpha-ray tube, phosphorescent screen, and low-power microscope—with which Rutherford won such fundamental results. The general set-up is one that has traditionally served well in British physics—simple means, sound foundation, convinced confidence, and genius.

The cloud chamber and the photographic plate are, between them, responsible for the discovery of all the new unstable elementary particles, which we are about to review, but one. The interpretation of the tracks recorded either in the cloud chamber or in the photographic emulsion is, needless to say, a matter of great skill and experience, but some rough rules may be indicated. The number of individual drops in the cloud trail or of individual grain-dots in the photographic track gives the amount of ionization and furnishes a clue to the nature of the particle. As an extreme case, fast electrons, as compared to heavy particles, leave a very sparse trail of ions, which can be identified in the cloud chamber but not in the emulsion. Otherwise particles which can be identified by one method can be identified by the other method. The length of the trail tells the energy of the particle. In the case of the cloud chamber the magnetic field gives the velocity, if the charge and mass are known: in the emulsion the tracks are too short for a practicable magnetic field to be helpful.

Records of impact also yield information. Neutrons, of course, produce no tracks themselves, since it is the influence of the electric charge that shakes electrons out of the atom, but their presence can be detected, because if a fast neutron hits a proton it will, in general, give it enough energy to produce a long track, which apparently starts from nothing in particular. Neutrons can also be identified by the reactions which they produce when caught by a heavy nucleus, since the result is the emission of charged, track-making particles. These few words give an indication of the kind of way in which the detective of the nuclear world has to reveal, record, and interpret the tracks with which he is concerned. The chief results of the investigations must be given without attempting to describe the often elaborate processes of reasoning by which they have been reached.

The first question is, what is the nature of the cosmic rays as they arrive from outer space? A study of their behaviour in the earth's magnetic field, which, of course, extends far beyond the atmosphere, has helped to answer this. For instance, the intensity of the radiation at sea-level is, on the whole, about 10 per cent less at the equator than at the poles, and there are other magnetic effects, which can be interpreted on the lines adopted to find the effect of the magnetic field in the mass spectrograph. It is now agreed that the primary cosmic radiation, whose transformations account for all the effects observed in the lower regions of the atmosphere, consists of nuclear particles—mostly protons but some heavier nuclei—of enormous energy, which bombard the outside of the atmosphere. There are not very many of these particles as atomic figures go: only a few arrive every second on a surface an inch square. Roughly speaking, they come from all directions. An expression of their small number is that, in spite of an energy per particle which is somewhere about a million million times that of a quantum of visible light, the energy of the cosmic radiation reaching the earth is about that of starlight.

There has been much speculation and calculation as to whence these particles come and what is the process that speeds them on their way. It has, for instance, been noted that occasionally, but not always, violent disturbances in the sun—the eruptions such as lead to great solar prominences —are accompanied by increases of cosmic ray activity on the earth. Nothing is certain, but the specialists in the field[5] incline to the belief that the radio stars, referred to in Chapter IV, are a main source and that, since it is extremely unlikely that high electrostatic fields can exist within our galaxy, magnetic fields are responsible for accelerating the particles until they have the enormous energies with which they strike the atmosphere—on the average 10,000 million electron volts, but in some cases up to 100,000 million electron volts and more. It has been shown, by rather complicated considerations, that changing magnetic fields in moving clouds of very thin, electrically conducting gas can, in certain circumstances, produce the required energies, and that the required circumstances may exist in violent solar eruptions, in radio stars, and in very tenuous regions of interstellar matter. It may seem strange to speak of matter in what is always called empty space, but the word 'empty' is justified, for it is estimated that there is about 1 atom per cubic centimetre between the stars in our galaxy, the milky way, as compared to about 50 million million million in the same volume of the atmosphere which we breathe.

Again, the magnetic field which the contemplated proc-

[5] At the moment of writing in 1955.

esses yield is very feeble, but the reason that these next-to-nothings produce an effect is to be found in the enormous distances in question. Our galaxy is a disc some 100,000 light years in diameter and a few thousand light years thick, a light year being the distance that light travels in a year. Light travels 156,000 miles a second and there are over thirty million seconds in a year. There is plenty of room for things to happen even if there is very little to make them happen.

Only a small fraction of the primary particles can come from the sun, for normally there is no appreciable difference between day and night in the number of particles striking the outer atmosphere. However, the behaviour of the small solar fraction has been an important guide in speculation as to the source of the particles.

The study of the effects of cosmic rays is an intensely active and extremely complicated subject. The complications are largely due to the great number of secondary effects, of a kind not even contemplated before the war, and to the birth and death of a large number of new, unstable elementary particles to which cosmic ray interactions can give rise. We will indicate roughly some of the observations in question and the kind of attempts being made to explain them, taking the observations first. Even at heights of 100,000 feet secondary radiations produced by the primary particles striking atmospheric atoms are present and even at terrestrial depths corresponding to nearly a mile of water cosmic rays, of such energy that they must be primary particles, penetrate. All through their path they are producing a diversity of effects.

As regards the primary particles, a favourable collision with a nucleus can lead to the complete explosion of one or both particles.

Typical complicated effects are observed in experiments at the earth's surface in which lead plates are put in the middle of the space in an expansion chamber. From such a plate an incident particle, whose track can be seen, produces a whole shower or cascade of tracks, due to secondary particles, which themselves have sufficient energy to produce other particles from nuclei, and so on, until the particles have lost the bulk of their energy in repeated transformations. The lead plates, for several may be put parallel to one another, supply in a short path plenty of heavy nuclei for the transmutations: showers have been detected in the atmosphere, but there counters hundreds of yards apart are used.

It has been shown that in the production of cascades an extraordinary mechanism is in question. Our fundamental tenets, to be kept in mind, are that mass and energy are equivalent: that radiation is emitted and absorbed in quanta whose energy is given by multiplying the frequency by an exceedingly small fixed number, Planck's constant: and that Nature delights in transmutations, as Newton said—especially in the neighbourhood of the nuclear field of force, which he could not know. According to recent theory the start of the whole process is an electron of very great energy, corresponding to thousands of millions of volts, probably produced by the impact of a very energetic particle on an atomic electron. This electron, in the process of being somewhat slowed down in its passage through matter, say the lead plate, produces a photon, which may also be called a high frequency radiation quantum or gamma ray. We now have, then, a concentration of high energy, without charge. This can change into two electrons (a positron and a 'negatron', or ordinary electron) of equal and opposite sign, for that represents no creation of charge and the mass of the two is the result of the conversion of energy of the photon, with plenty of energy left over for energy of motion. Each of these two electrons, in slowing down, produces a photon, very energetic but, of course, not so energetic as the first photon, and this in turn produces a pair of fresh electrons of opposite charge.

A few figures may be useful here. The energy-mass relation shows that the mass of an electron is equivalent to the energy acquired by an electron in a fall of 512,000 volts. The mass of a pair of electrons, then, needs for its formation an energy of 1,024,000 electron volts. If we start with a primary particle of energy of 1000 million electron volts there is plenty of room for slowing down, for the formation of radiation quanta, and for losses before the last pair of electrons is formed.

Cosmic rays lead, then, to the formation of a positive electron, to the materialization of energy, and to the energization of mass. But we have still to consider the family of new unstable particles, of mass between that of the electron and that of the proton; particles positive, negative, and neutral, which go under the name 'mesons'.[6] The word is derived from the Greek *mesos*, 'the middle': the prefix *meso* always denotes 'middle', as in *mesothorax*, the middle of the three segments of the thorax of an insect, and here means 'a midway mass'. There are also some unstable particles called 'hyperons', from Greek *hyper*, 'above', since their mass is above that of the neutron, but less than that of the deuteron.

The first of these particles to be identified was what is now called the mu-meson, the Greek letter $\mu$ (mu) having been originally used to denote it. It was discovered by C. D. Anderson and S. H. Neddermeyer from photographic records of a cloud chamber, in a magnetic field, exposed on Pike's Peak in Colorado (14,108 feet). They found tracks which were short, due to particles which were heavy and positively charged, but the curvature of the track in the magnetic field, the length and the drop density, which, it will be remembered, are determining factors in enabling mass to be deduced, showed that the particle in question must be much heavier than an electron, but lighter than a proton, and therefore new. It was positively charged and the mass given as about 200 times that of the electron. To-day the figure is believed to be 210 and negative mu-mesons have also been discovered. Mu-mesons are present at sea-level as well as at higher altitudes.

Powell, Occhialini and Lattes, as a result of their intensive

[6] Originally the name 'mesotron' was proposed, but it is little used nowadays. However, if the reader meets with it, another new particle is not in question.

photo-emulsion work, discovered a particle of somewhat greater mass, 276 times that of the electron, to which the name pi-meson (from the Greek letter $\pi$) has been given. It seems that the pi-meson can change into the mu-meson, the difference of mass being converted into energy of motion, another of these extraordinary transformations. In the nuclear world mass and energy appear to transform as freely as work and heat in the old-time tangible world. Pi-mesons can be not only positively and negatively charged, but neutral. When charged, the charge is always the electronic charge in magnitude—at least that appears to be assumed for all mesons.

The photo-emulsion work has led to the discovery of still further mesons, named tau ($\tau$), kappa ($\kappa$), and chi ($\chi$) mesons, of masses about 966 in terms of the electron mass, some positive, some negative, some neutral. The proton, let us remember, has mass 1836 electron-masses. Another class of new particle has mass about 2200 and goes into the general class of hyperon. Various transmutations of these particles have been, and are being, studied. There is no point in giving a mass of detail here, more especially as the notation is not yet settled and fresh particles may be discovered by the time that this is read. All that is desired to do is to indicate the kind of new venture on which physics has embarked, the multiplicity of new particles that have to be ordered and explained. A word about general theory will come later, when we have seen what the theories have to account for.

Now there is one point that separates the old particles—electron, proton, deuteron, alpha particle—from the new particles, the positron and those that have just been briefly reviewed. The old ones were stable and persisted in their nature and their masses: protons might, of course, pair off with electrons, but apparently they kept their individuality and only comparatively small changes in energy, calculable in terms of old-style electrical attractions, were involved. The new particles are all unstable and figures have been found for their average lifetimes, ranging from a few millionths of a second for mu-mesons to less than a million-millionth of a second for neutral pi-mesons. The positron likewise has a very short, if indefinite life, for as soon as it approaches an electron, which is usually pretty soon, it combines with it and vanishes as a positron: the result of the disappearance of the two oppositely charged electrons is two equal gamma-ray photons going in opposite directions. This creation of two photons has been observed and there are beautiful photographs, taken with a cloud chamber in a magnetic field, showing the inverse effect, the creation of a positive and of a negative electron pair from a unit of radiation. The radiation produced by the disappearance of an electron pair is often called 'annihilation radiation', but it is really transformation radiation, the energy of mass being changed into energy of radiation. A tendency to transform their nature in the strong nuclear field is a characteristic of all ultimate particles.

The various great machines, cyclotrons, synchrotons, synchrocyclotrons, and so on, which have been used to produce jets of very energetic particles, bear to the cosmic rays much the same relation as Cockcroft and Walton's original particle accelerator did to the alpha rays used by Rutherford and his contemporaries—they produce an immensely more plentiful supply of particles but the individual energy of each particle is far less than that of the swiftest particles provided by Nature. The artificially produced particles include, in particular, fast protons, deuterons, and alpha particles. Through these, very energetic gamma rays and neutrons are produced, and high energy neutrons are particularly effective for nuclear attack, on account of their lack of charge and because their equivalent wave-length, by the de Broglie formula, is within the range of nuclear forces. For an energy of 90 MeV, for instance, this wave-length is a tenth of a million-millionth of a centimetre.

Fast neutrons cannot, of course, be produced by direct action of accelerating electric forces, since there is no electric charge by which to catch hold of them, but are obtained from fast deuterons, which are a favourite projectile for nuclear work. It will be shown, when we come to consider nuclear theory, that on the scale concerned in these nuclear changes, it does not take much energy to make a deuteron split into a neutron and a proton, and fast deuterons are stripped, as the phrase goes, when they strike the nuclei of a target. The neutron flies on with high energy. In particular the Berkeley 184-inch cyclotron has been used to produce in this way very powerful neutron beams.

The scattering of energetic neutrons by protons, which in practice means by paraffin wax or some such solid containing plenty of combined hydrogen, and the scattering of proton beams by protons, is a fruitful method of investigating the structure of the nucleus and has been the subject of an immense amount of work. It may give some notion of the activity in the nuclear field to mention that a report printed in 1952 on high-energy neutron and proton scattering alone cited over eighty original contributions on the subject. Even the briefest summary of the work involves difficult technical detail. As regards the subject of energy levels in light nuclei, concerning which this type of scattering contributes information, a list of pertinent papers published in 1950 ran to over a thousand titles. Presumably many physicists have read them all, but at half an hour each it would take ten good working weeks.

These accelerator investigations may be called nuclear laboratory work, as distinct from the relatively large-scale processes in the atomic pile installations, described in the next chapter, which may be called nuclear production work. This situation is in some respects similar to that in organic chemistry a hundred years ago, when a large number of natural compounds were known, and the laboratory synthesis of desired compounds was being rapidly developed, according to rules which were being established. The main building stones were few—carbon, hydrogen, oxygen, and nitrogen atoms—in place of the nuclear synthesizer's two, proton and neutron, but even with only carbon and hydrogen much was done by the organic chemist. Likewise, industrial organic work, the large-scale manufacture of dyes, was beginning to correspond to our atomic piles. To-day the ability to build at will nuclei up to a certain size is being established, and who would be willing to say definitely that the ability to stabilize nuclei made up of assemblies of particles at present known only in unstable forms will never be acquired? Already it is possible to make the same compound nucleus in more than one way.

Further, just as in organic chemistry, certain compounds, called isomers, are well known which, although made up of the same atoms, each kind present in the same numbers, have different properties,[7] nuclei have been made which contain the same number of protons and of neutrons, and yet have different properties. An example is a particular isotope, mass 80, of bromine, nuclear charge 35, which has two isomeric forms, both decaying radio-actively, but in a different manner and with different half lives. This shows that the same collection of protons and neutrons can, in fairly heavy nuclei, be put together in different ways to form a nucleus, just as the same collection of carbon and hydrogen atoms can be put together differently in certain organic compounds. This possibility of nuclear isomers is a good indication of the complications of nuclear structure.

One of the earliest and simplest unstable isotopes was made by Rutherford, Oliphant, and Harteck with one of the early accelerators, with what to-day would be considered a trivial potential of 400,000 volts. By bombarding deuterons, compactly contained in a solid compound of heavy hydrogen, with deuterons, they obtained a new isotope of hydrogen, with mass of 3 atomic units, and nuclear charge, of course, 1. The odd proton was expelled. This isotope, which turns up frequently in nuclear work to-day, is called tritium,

---

[7] A simple example is afforded by n-butane and iso-butane, n standing for normal. The molecule in each case consists of 4 carbon atoms and 10 hydrogen atoms: in the n form the 4 carbon atoms are arranged in a row, in the iso form 3 are in a row and 1 to the side. Unfortunately, by a notation dating from days long before the atomic nucleus was discovered, the arrangement of the 4 carbon atoms is called the butane nucleus, which might prove confusing.

the third one, and to its nucleus has been given the classical name triton.[8] The same deuteron-on-deuteron impact, produced by a large cyclotron, can lead to an isotope, of mass 3, of helium, but, of course, whereas the nucleus of the 3 isotope of hydrogen consists of 2 neutrons and 1 proton, that of the helium isotope consists of 1 neutron and 2 protons. The triton is not stable, but sends out in the course of time—the half life is many years—a low energy negative electron, which means that a proton has become a neutron, so that the result is a stable 3-helium nucleus. This is just a simple example of nuclear manufacture and change.

Obviously one can only mention a few typical examples of nuclear laboratory work. Mesons have been artificially produced, in the first place by a beam of 380 million electron-volt particles from the Berkeley synchrocyclotron. It is, of course, very helpful to have a copious supply of the particles to hand rather than to have to wait for sparse deliveries from outer space, but for the highest energy particles we still have to rely on nature. The shattering of the nucleus into a large number of particles, first observed with cosmic rays, has now also been produced in the laboratory, for the first time at Berkeley, where so much pioneering work has been done. When it comes to nuclear hunting the Berkeley boys certainly have the experienced game wardens *and* the guns.

While this book was in the press, at the end of 1955, the discovery of a new atomic particle, the anti-proton, or negative proton, was announced by the University of California and the U.S. Atomic Energy Commission. The latter body described it as 'a nuclear ghost which had haunted the world's physicists for a generation', meaning that theory, initiated by Dirac, had for that period indicated that there should be such a particle, while hitherto there had been no evidence for its real existence. The phrase may also be taken to signify that while it is not a component of the nucleus, which consists of protons and neutrons, it is a shadowy

[8] 'Or hear old Triton blow his wreathed horn.'—Wordsworth.

counterpart of the proton. It is created in the process of collision when particles of sufficiently high energy are involved. The new particle was discovered when protons accelerated to about 6 GeV (6000 MeV) by the bevatron were shot onto a copper target in the vacuum chamber. Among the fragmentation products the negative proton was identified by its mass, ascertained by a special arrangement of magnetic fields and scintillation counters of the new type to which reference has been made. There are comparatively very few such particles created and that they were not found before is due to the immense particle energy required to produce them, which the bevatron makes available. Just as the discovery of the positive electron followed at a long interval that of the negative electron, so the discovery of the negative proton has followed at a long interval that of the positive proton.

Shattering into many fragments is now called *spallation*, not from the Greek or Latin, but from the word *spall*, of doubtful origin, meaning, in mining, 'to break into small pieces'.

An outstanding result of the high energy particle work is the manufacture of elements beyond uranium, which up to the beginning of the late war represented the heaviest and most complex element known. Uranium, atomic number 92, commonest isotope of mass number 238—there are now 14 isotopes known, including the manufactured ones—is, of course, unstable, but still found in Nature because of its extremely slow rate of decay. The elements of higher atomic number, which, it will be remembered, means of higher nuclear charge, are called by the general name transuranium elements. They are all unstable, with half lives generally not exceeding hundreds of years, and even the extreme case, plutonium 239, has the brief half life, when the age of the world is considered, of some 25,000 years. That is why these elements do not exist in Nature: if they were made when the rest of the world's elements were manufactured, they have fallen to pieces ages ago, giving rise to lighter and more stable elements. Reckoning the extremely slow decay of uranium as near-enough stability, we may sum up by saying that uranium, atomic number 92, represents the highest atomic number that is stable—or nearly stable.

The trans-uranium elements have been made mainly by the efforts of E. M. McMillan and G. T. Seaborg and their expert collaborators at Berkeley. The work is characterized not only by the enormous energies of the projectiles concerned, up to 40 million electron volts or so, and their plentiful supply, but also by the extraordinarily delicate chemical operations necessary to identify the substances produced. In conventional chemical analysis methods have been developed which enable quantities of a few milligrams to be handled satisfactorily, the technique going under the general name of microchemistry. In this trans-uranium chemistry the quantities available are often a few millionths rather than a few thousandths of a gram. If this seems a very small weight to make with so much effort, it should be remembered that a millionth of a gram represents a few hundred million million of the heavy atoms in question.

The chemical operations concerned are characterized by the extremely small amounts of liquid used, which may be as little as is in a drop the size of a full stop. Dissolved in such a volume millionths of a gram make quite a strong solution, but handling such quantities of liquid is a delicate matter. The 'test-tubes' are made from fine capillary tubing and the manipulation is done under a microscope. This new technique is known as ultra-microchemistry. It would have been more logical, perhaps, to call milligram chemistry, millichemistry, and this microgram chemistry simply microchemistry, but it is too late to do that now.

The work of manufacturing trans-uranium elements is very elaborate, fast neutrons, protons, deuterons, and helium nuclei having been used as projectiles. All that can be done here is to list the new elements which have been manufactured. They are, in order of increasing atomic number, given in brackets: neptunium (93), plutonium (94), americium (95), curium (96), berkelium (97), californium (98), einsteinium (99), fermium (100), and mendelevium (101).

The general properties are very complicated. It might be thought at first, for instance, that the heavier the new element the more unstable it would be, that is, the less its half life. But things are not so simple as that. For most of the elements in question a great variety of isotopes has been already found, and the half lives of the different isotopes vary enormously. Plutonium, for instance, has some twelve isotopes, one of which, the plutonium 239 already cited, has far the longest half life of any of the trans-uranium elements, while for one of the others the half life is a minute fraction of a second. Altogether, with their isotopes, of which in all over fifty have been found at the time of writing, their extraordinary variety of stability and their various methods of formation and decay, the trans-uranium elements make a formidable and fascinating study.

We now come to consider the general properties of the nucleus. It is obvious that it must have laws of its own, different from those of classical physics, since it is an assembly of positively charged protons and neutral neutrons. On the classical laws of electricity there would be, at the small distances in question, very strong repulsive forces between the positive charges, counterbalanced by no attractive forces of any kind, so that the whole structure would be violently driven asunder. Rutherford clearly foresaw this difficulty and stated as early as 1913, with his usual comprehension and clarity, 'It would appear as if the positively charged atoms of matter attract one another at very small distances, for otherwise it is difficult to see how the component parts at the centre are held together'. This is in accord with the conclusions of most recent theory.

It was shown by experiments of Rutherford and his school on the scattering of alpha particles that the Coulomb law, which gives the force that prevails between electric charges at normal distances, broke down for very close approach between the particle and the struck nucleus. It is usual in talking of the size of the nucleus to regard as its boundary the surface at which deviations from Coulomb's law become appreciable: this will clearly vary a little according to the meaning attached to 'appreciable', but not much, for the deviations become large quite suddenly. The boundary is something like the boundary of a city, which now that cities are no longer walled has no precise position, but about which everybody would agree within fairly close limits.

Rutherford, who died in 1937, concluded that the nuclei of light atoms were about $5 \times 10^{-13}$ cm. ($\frac{1}{5}$ of a million-millionth of an inch) across, which agrees roughly with more recent estimates. From experiments on the scattering of alpha particles and, more precisely, with fast neutrons, which have the advantages already indicated, it has been deduced that the radius of the proton itself is $1.4 \times 10^{-13}$ cm. (about $1/20$ of a million-millionth of an inch), and further, which is very important, that the volume of the nuclei of heavier atoms is proportional to their mass, which means that the radius of the gold nucleus comes out to be $8.1 \times 10^{-13}$ cm. (about $\frac{1}{3}$ of a million-millionth of an inch). This proportionality of volume to number of nucleons implies that we must consider the nucleons to be very tightly packed, each taking up about the space indicated by the volume of the isolated proton.

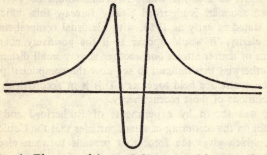

FIG. 4. *The general form of the potential barrier which surrounds a heavy nucleus*

Considering first of all the action of the nucleus on a charged particle which is just outside it, either a particle shot at it or a particle which has somehow appeared from inside, there is a very strong electric field which, as already mentioned, is described by talking of a potential barrier, a smooth surrounding wall with a cross-section similar to that shown in the diagram (Fig. 4). Taking gravitational potential in place of electric potential, a smooth sphere just outside the summit will run down, gathering energy all the time until the flat is reached: a sphere speeded over the surface towards the nucleus will be turned aside if not aimed at the centre and, if aimed at the centre, will run up the side and surmount the summit if sufficiently energetic, and run up the side, stop, and run back if not sufficiently energetic. That was the old, classical picture. As was indicated when Cockcroft and Walton's experiments were discussed, modern theory leads to the conclusion that there is a chance of a particle finding a way through the potential barrier, a chance vanishingly small if the particle has little energy, but rapidly increasing as the energy increases. We used the rough picture of tunnels through the potential barrier.

To explain the close co-existence of the protons within the nucleus, to account for the stability of a structure which on the older views is essentially unstable, clearly demands some radically new conception of force, characterized by, among other qualities, the fact that it becomes considerable only at very close distances. This new type of force is called an exchange force and was first introduced to explain how it is that two exactly similar atoms can combine to form a molecule. As the simplest case, consider a hydrogen molecule which is ionized, that is, has lost an electron and so consists of one electron and two protons, which are somehow held together, although, of course, at a distance vastly greater than that which separates two protons which are in one nucleus. Heitler and London explained this cohesion on the basis of wave mechanics, expressing mathematically a process involving the exchange of the electron from the dominance of one nucleus to that of the other. It is not easy to interpret in general language why the exchange holds the nuclei together, but, for that matter, it was not easy to explain, on the classical theory, why a force of attraction prevailed between a positive and a negative charge, although the attraction could be expressed in terms of strains in a medium, as was the repulsion of an electron for a like electron.

An expression of this repulsion is to-day likewise given in terms of exchange forces: a photon is tossed from electron to interacting electron. In general circumstances these photons, like cheques passed backwards and forwards between two firms to constitute their relation to one another, do not come into circulation, but in other circumstances, in the presence of nuclear forces in one case and the presence of market forces, let us say, in the other case, the photons or the cash do come into circulation.

The exchange forces needed to hold together the nucleus are of a new type, introduced by the Japanese physicist Yukawa. For certain complicated reasons, involving among other considerations the fact that the forces between the nucleons fall off so rapidly with distance, the intermediary particles in the nuclear exchange cannot, he showed, be electrons, which give fields far too small, but must possess much greater mass. The mass required turned out to be about 200 times that of the electron, and was assumed to characterize a hypothetical particle to which the name meson was first applied. At the time when Yukawa's theory was put forward there was no direct evidence for a particle of this intermediate mass, but to-day, as we have seen, the investigation of cosmic rays has revealed mesons of many different types, all of very short life, and the properties of Yukawa's mesons appear to agree best with those of the pi-mesons.

On the meson theory there are exchange forces of attraction between juxtaposed protons, juxtaposed neutrons, and neutron-proton neighbours. The theory of the forces between closely packed nucleons is a very complicated matter: Yukawa in his 1949 Nobel Prize discourse said, 'In this way, meson theory has changed a great deal during these fifteen years', and the change has gone on since.

In dealing with nuclear matter there are other terms that

will meet the student approaching this romantic subject. The ultimate particles have a property to which the name 'spin' (an international word in this connection) has been given. As was mentioned when spectra were discussed, Uhlenbeck and Goudsmit found that certain difficulties in the theory of optical spectra could be surmounted by supposing that the electrons in the atom had a spin about their axes, like the daily rotation of the earth: this confers the property of behaving like minute magnets and, as in one atom there can be electrons spinning in either of two directions, like tops started with a right-hand or left-hand twist, it also gives two possible states for each electron, which theory needs. All ultimate particles now have a spin quantum.

Further, when the varied energy of the beta rays from radioactive atoms is considered, difficulties appear which have been solved (or avoided or dodged, according to the philosophic outlook of the writer) by the invention of a new entity, called the neutrino. It is neutral and has very little or no mass—hence, supposedly, the name; the beginning suggests neutrality and the termination diminutiveness or lightness—but it has been endowed with the property of carrying energy and spin: in short, when there is something wrong in the balance of energy or angular momentum, the neutrino is invoked to account for it. To-day there is, too, an antineutrino, differing from the neutrino in the sense of its spin, whose vanity must be satisfied with this brief mention.

It is accepted to-day, then, that the nucleons in a heavy nucleus are held together by exchange forces, operating between neighbouring particles. This means that a nucleon in the interior of the nucleus is pulled equally in all directions, whereas a nucleon at the surface is pulled inwards. There is, therefore, a surface effect, which tends to make the nucleus have a spherical shape. We have, then, a dense assembly of particles, practically touching one another, held by intense local forces, which confer a special surface energy. But this is exactly what we have in a water drop—a close assembly of water molecules, with a special surface energy which finds its expression in the surface tension, the force which tends to make a soap bubble contract and to make a drop spherical. A liquid drop, in fact, gives a very good picture of the nucleus, as originally pointed out by Niels Bohr in 1936. The immense amount of work carried out on the subject since that time has confirmed the general helpfulness of his view.

The nucleons include, of course, electrically charged particles which are not normally represented among the molecules of a drop. The ordinary electric forces between their charges are very small compared to the exchange forces at the distance between two neighbouring nucleons, but they conspire to create the potential barrier, for the exchange forces die off very rapidly and at the distance of the barrier the electric forces preponderate. Even within the nucleus the electric forces have a minor but significant part to play.

We have already noted that the volume of a nucleus is, at any rate roughly, proportional to the number of particles contained, which supports the drop theory. Incidentally, the density of the nucleus, which is, if one may use the phrase, all mass and no empty space, is some 500 million million times that of a water drop. Obviously a very important nuclear figure is the binding energy or the energy required to take the nucleus apart into particles widely separated from one another.[9] The stability of the nucleus is the greater the greater the binding energy.

How can we find the binding energy? We do not know enough about details of nuclear force to calculate it with certainty, but that is not necessary. When we have to find the energy change attending the formation of a chemical compound from its elements—the so-called molecular heat of formation, which is the chemical analogue of the nuclear

[9] The binding energy is usually defined as the energy required to put the nucleus together and then, of course, comes out to be negative. The figure, without the negative sign, is then taken as the binding energy. There are certain reasons for doing this, but they are purely formal, and it is simpler to do what is here adopted, which comes to the same thing in the end.

characteristic now being considered—we do not calculate the forces between the atoms, but measure in the laboratory the heat liberated when the chemical combinations concerned take place. This heat can be expressed in any other units of energy desired, in ergs or in foot pounds. In the nuclear case we use the change of mass which takes place when the nucleus is formed from its constituents, which is the equivalent of a precise amount of energy. We do not actually build the compound nucleus in question: rather, its mass is measured as described in Chapter VIII. The masses of the protons and neutrons that compose it are known. It is then a simple matter of arithmetic to calculate the change of mass attending formation.

Let us take the simplest example. The mass of the proton is 1.00758 atomic mass units, of the neutron 1.00895 a.m.u. A proton and a neutron, if brought so close that they adhere, form a deuteron, the nucleus of the heavy hydrogen atom. The mass of the two separate particles is 2.01653, while the mass of the deuteron, as measured by its behaviour in the electric and magnetic field, is 2.01419, which means a loss of mass of 0.00234 a.m.u. attending the formation of the nucleus. This is equivalent to an energy of about 2.2 million electron volts which, to take a chemical standard of comparison, is about 250,000 times the energy linkage of hydrogen atom to hydrogen atom in the hydrogen molecule.

If we turn to the alpha particle, we have to imagine the putting together of two protons and two neutrons, whose separated masses add up to 4.03306 a.m.u. But the mass of the normal helium nucleus is 4.00279, which is less by 0.03027 a.m.u. This represents 28.2 million electron volts, or roughly 7 million electron volts per particle, and shows the great stability of the alpha particle and why it stands so much knocking about without coming to pieces.

If we are concerned with the release of energy attending nuclear buildings up and breakings down, it is most useful to have the binding energy per particle, since the number of particles in the compound and simpler nuclei considered in a transformation will be the same. For instance, if what

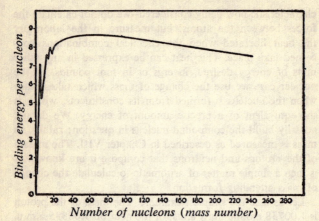

*Number of nucleons (mass number)*

FIG. 5. *The binding energy per nucleon for nuclei of various masses. The unit of energy is the million-electron-volt. The large peak on the extreme left corresponds to helium, mass 4*

is in question is the splitting of a nucleus of mass number 235 into smaller nuclei, the number of particles in all the smaller nuclei, including any odd nucleons shed, must add up to 235. A general knowledge of the energy per particle in the region concerned will indicate the change of energy attending regrouping.

The general course of the binding energy per particle as deduced from measurements of the masses of isotopes is shown in Fig. 5 plotted against the number of particles (neutrons and protons) in the nucleus. There are details in the behaviour of nuclei of odd and even and fourfold numbers, and so on, that have, for simplicity, been omitted. From this diagram a remarkable result is at once clear; in the region where the number of particles is less than 40 or so, building up a nucleus from the lightest particles leads to a decrease of mass, but in the region of the heavy nuclei, breaking up a nucleus into lighter fractions leads to a decrease of mass. Decrease of mass is liberation of energy.

This can be briefly expressed by saying that the *fusion* of the lightest nuclei and the *fission* of the heaviest nuclei provides atomic—or better, nuclear—energy.

The general reason for this behaviour can be seen without too much difficulty. If only the special nuclear forces—the exchange forces—were in question, then the packing fraction would, within a small fraction, be the same for all nuclei, and the curve of Fig. 5 would be replaced by a horizontal straight line. Fission or fusion would lead to hardly any change of mass. The sharp rise of the actual curve on the left is due to the surface forces which have been mentioned. The energy which these forces contribute per particle is relatively very much more important when the nucleus is very small, just as with a liquid drop the surface energy per unit mass is very much greater when the drops are minute. The slow rise from the extreme right to the maximum is mainly due to the electric forces of repulsion, which thus have something to say, although they are small compared to the special nuclear forces.

We have, then, two kinds of nuclear processes that will lead to the liberation of vast amounts of energy, a building up from very light nuclei or a splitting of very heavy nuclei. A rough analogy from ordinary processes is the explosion of hydrogen and oxygen gas, which builds up a heavier molecule with release of energy, or the breaking up of a molecule of an unstable nature, such as mercury fulminate, which, on slight provocation, splits into atomic parts with the release of energy. Although processes which lead to a release of energy often take place slowly by themselves, as in the case of mercury fulminate, which decomposes slowly in storage, and in the case of radioactive elements, which spontaneously transform, nevertheless in general, some external shock is necessary to initiate the process. Something has already been said about the shock needed in the nuclear case.

Returning to our analogy, a drop may lose particles by evaporation or it may vibrate and break into two, as can often be seen at a tap. The evaporation is a consequence of the heat agitation: the hotter the liquid the larger the probability of a molecule breaking loose from the attractive forces. Both evaporation and division have their counterparts in the nucleus.

When a particle, either a neutron or a sufficiently energetic light nucleus, enters the compact nucleus, it shares its energy with all the nucleons. A rough expression of what happens is to say that the nucleus is heated up, just as a liquid drop would be if somehow or other it stopped a very minute bullet. Dividing the energy by the number of nucleons we find that, to have the energy per particle corresponding to the nuclear gain, the temperature, as ordinarily calculated, would have to be some ten thousand million degrees. It is in this sense that the expression 'heated up' is used, but the state of affairs contemplated is that within a single nucleus and is not the same thing as the temperature in, say, the interior of a star.

What will happen to the heated nucleus depends upon its temperature, in the sense indicated, and upon its constitution. As we have seen, if a very large amount of energy be added suddenly, as in certain cosmic-ray reactions, it may very quickly evaporate as a whole, splitting, in the process of spallation, into as many as forty parts. Or it may, when less added energy is in question, quickly expel a particle, either a meson, or a proton, or a heavier nucleus, or a quantum of very high frequency radiation. Or it may, in the case of artificial radioactivity, expel a particle after an average delay which may vary from a fraction of a second to years. The search for rules that shall determine, from the structure of the nucleus and the energy and nature of the impinging particle, what will occur occupies the attention of some of the world's leading theoretical physicists. Much has been done: there are distinctions, for instance, between nuclei containing odd and even numbers of nucleons; there is a complicated scheme of nuclear energy levels. When we think that the properties of even the simplest liquids, in the normal physical sense, are imperfectly understood, the difficulties that the nuclear liquid offers do not need emphasizing. In physics, proximity is perplexity and the nucleus is particle proximity in the highest possible degree.

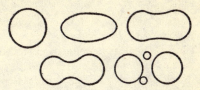

FIG. 6. *The drop model of the nucleus. Successive stages of the break-up, or fission, into two more or less equal parts, with surplus neutrons*

When we come to very heavy nuclei, large nuclear drops, the process corresponding to the break-up of a liquid drop into two main parts can take place. In a nucleus with a large charge the electric repulsions become considerable and, if a state of vibration is produced by the impact of a particle or by addition of energy imparted by the presence of a strange neutron, may suffice to tear the nucleus into two, with an odd fragment or fragments over. Fig. 6 shows the kind of process that is imagined to take place. First of all a neck is formed and then two main parts, not quite equal, appear, with one or more odd neutrons, which are superfluous when the protons and neutrons in these two nuclei are counted up and compared with those of the original nucleus. It is a simple picture of the most terrifying process known to man, compared to which the old 15-inch gun is a harmless toy.

# CHAPTER X

# About Applications
# of Nuclear Transformation

In cosmic-ray reactions and in the transformation produced by artificially accelerated particles we have, generally speaking, one nucleus transformed for each impact of a nuclear missile. It is true that in cosmic-ray showers many nuclei suffer change, but even here each small group of processes requires a separate start. There is no sustained reaction: in all forms of particle accelerator the total energy supplied to, and dissipated by, the machine is immensely greater than the amount of energy released as a result of the loss of mass in the nuclear reactions provoked.

As regards release of energy, a somewhat similar situation would be presented by a man who, in primitive times, had succeeded, by rotating a stick in a depression—a cyclic process!—in getting wood hot enough for it to glow locally by combination with the air without ever catching fire, that is without the combustion spreading. He would have demonstrated in principle the possibility of obtaining light and heat energy from chemical change, but only by supplying energy vastly in excess of that released by that change. To obtain light and heat profitably from the energy of chemical combinations he would have to learn to build a pile in which the heat of parts where combustion had been started would cause neighbouring parts in their turn to burn, deliver heat, and ignite still other parts. This corresponds to what has now been done in the nuclear case: we have learnt how to provoke a nuclear reaction in such a way that, of itself, it leads to other nuclear reactions, so that the process spontaneously spreads.

Here again problems are raised that find a simple illustration in the world of ordinary, as against nuclear, chemistry. With coke and air the combustion takes place slowly and in a way that can be controlled by such means as varying the draught. This combustion is a suitable process for ordinary domestic or industrial uses—cooking food or smelting iron. With charcoal mixed with nitre and sulphur, to form gunpowder, the combustion takes place very rapidly: the energy released per ounce of powder is much less than that released by the burning of an ounce of charcoal, but the release is sudden, violent, and uncontrolled. This is a suitable process for death and destruction. It is, however, perhaps worth remembering that ordinary explosives such as gunpowder, but more usually compositions containing nitroglycerine or trinitrotoluene, can be used for peaceful purposes, such as blasting rock. Possibly it will later be found safe and profitable to apply explosive nuclear reactions, as used in the atomic bomb, to really large-scale blasting operations, especially in remote parts of the earth.

The possibilities of producing nuclear energy on a large scale depend upon the effectiveness of the neutron as an agent for provoking nuclear change. This was first realized by Fermi, the brilliant investigator who died in November 1954 at the age of fifty-three.[1] He saw that, while the neutron sources then available—beryllium powder bombarded with alpha particles from radon enclosed with it—were feeble, at the same time neutrons had a great advantage over alpha particles and other charged particles in their very long range and the fact that they were not electrically re-

[1] In a letter written to the present author in 1936, Rutherford said, 'The main merit of Fermi was his rapid trial whether neutrons would produce radioactive bodies, immediately after the Curie-Joliot discovery'. In the next eighteen years Fermi was to acquire much further merit.

pelled by nuclei in their path. He and his collaborators in 1934 produced a whole series of new artificially radioactive atoms by exposing different elements to neutrons, which mostly had a very high energy, corresponding to that which a proton would acquire under a push of some millions of volts.

Then, as a result of chance observation and experimental genius, there came an astonishing discovery. It appeared that it made a difference whether a silver cylinder that was being tested for artificial radioactivity, and the neutron source that was irradiating it, stood on a wooden table or on a piece of metal. After trying the effect of lead round the source Fermi decided to try in its place a very light substance, paraffin wax. To the astonishment of the laboratory this increased the effect of the neutrons enormously, up to a hundred times.[2] Fermi soon had the explanation. When a neutron hits a light nucleus, then, supposing that it is not absorbed, it rebounds like one billiard ball hitting another, and gives part of its energy to the struck nucleus. The lighter the struck nucleus, the bigger the fraction of the energy which it takes over. By repeated impacts the energy of motion of the neutron may be reduced until it has no more than the ordinary energy of thermal movement of the atoms among which it moves. Neutrons that have been slowed down in this way are called 'thermal neutrons' and are sometimes said to have been 'thermalized'. For the purpose in hand, the paraffin wax, which is a combination of hydrogen and carbon, is merely a mass of hydrogen nuclei.

Thermal neutrons enter readily into complex nuclei and cause instability, so that they are particularly effective in producing certain types of nuclear change. They not only change normal atoms into artificially radioactive ones but are, as will be seen later, particularly effective in producing

[2] This incident is given as an example of the way in which fundamental discoveries can still be made by following up a chance observation. It is graphically described in Laura Fermi's *Atoms in the Family,* a most entertaining account of her husband's brilliant career.

nuclear fission in certain cases. In general, the probability of a neutron reacting with a nucleus depends upon the nature of the nucleus, the particular transmutation in question, and the velocity of the neutron. A certain particular velocity is often particularly effective, just as a certain particular frequency of sound wave or light wave awakens response in a body naturally adapted to vibrate with that frequency, the phenomenon known as resonance. In view of what has been said of the wave nature of particles this is not particularly surprising.

The intensive study of the transformations produced by slow neutrons led to the discovery of nuclear fission, which was the starting-point of the investigations that culminated in the wholesale release of nuclear energy. In all the considerable number of transmutations produced in the early experiments on bombarding elements with neutrons, the new atoms that had been made were either isotopes of the bombarded atoms or near neighbours in the periodic table. It was a question of adding or subtracting one or two nucleons, and this kind of change was what was always anticipated. Fermi and others bombarded uranium in the hope of making transuranium elements, of the kind described in the last chapter, and thought that they had done so, but there were some very puzzling features of the experiments. However, as the result of concentrated research in the difficult subject of radio chemistry, of which Hahn had had long experience, he and Strassmann showed in 1939, some months before the outbreak of war, that what actually happened was something quite different. The uranium nucleus was not modified by the addition or loss of an odd neutron or proton, but was actually broken into two parts of roughly equal mass, one being, in a particular case, an isotope of barium, with atomic number 56. It has since been shown that various types of fission, resulting in different medium-mass nuclei, can be produced, but the general features of the transformation are the same in all cases.

There are two fundamental processes to be considered when a uranium nucleus is thus fissioned. One is the release of a very large amount of energy, consequent on the decrease of mass: disappearance of mass means the appearance of an equivalent quantity of energy. This is expressed in the right-hand side of Fig. 5. The other process is the emission of fast neutrons, as first proved by Joliot, Halban and Kowarski. More than one neutron is ejected for each fission: the average number is about 2.5. It is this that gives the possibility of a chain reaction, since with this number, even allowing for losses and ineffective capture, each fission is capable of provoking at least one other fission. Start the process, and it continues indefinitely—or at any rate as long as there are sufficient fissionable nuclei about.

Before we turn to the construction of the atomic bomb and of the atomic pile we have to consider briefly the behaviour of the different isotopes of uranium to neutrons of different speeds. Natural uranium, of atomic number 92, consists of three isotopes, of atomic mass 234, 235, and 238, but 234 is present to the extent of only six parts in a hundred thousand and may be left out of account. Uranium 235 constitutes just over 0.7 per cent, but is of the greatest importance for our purpose, and uranium 238 makes up the rest.

It is the uranium 235 that is fissioned and slow neutrons that are most effective in provoking the fission, in particular thermal neutrons. Faster neutrons also produce fission, but, generally speaking, the greater the speed the less the effect. However, the fission of 235 by neutrons as they are emitted from fissioned atoms, without being slowed down, is of prime importance for the atomic bomb.

Uranium 238 is not fissioned by slow neutrons, but only by fast neutrons, and even they are not very efficient as fission-provokers. Uranium 238 does, however, readily capture a slowish neutron and become the heavier isotope 239, which is not stable, but gives out an electron and so becomes a nucleus with one more unit of positive charge, since loss of a negative charge is equivalent to gain of a positive charge. The element of nuclear charge—atomic number—93 is, as was mentioned in the last chapter, neptunium. It too is unstable, giving out an electron and becoming a new element of atomic number 94, plutonium. The half life of uranium 239 is only 23 minutes: of neptunium 23 days: of plutonium 24,000 years, which means that, as far as storage purposes are concerned, the last named can be regarded as stable. At the same time this half life is very small when compared to the age of the earth, which explains why plutonium is not found in nature. Plutonium behaves to neutrons, slow and fast, much as does uranium 235. In particular, it can be fissioned by fast neutrons.

When we say that uranium 238 captures slowish neutrons we mean those with an energy of a few electron volts. Now the energy of a thermal neutron is much less than this, about 1/25 electron volt. Such neutrons are not absorbed by uranium 238.

Suppose, then, that we have lumps of ordinary uranium, that is, of 238 with a small proportion of 235, and that they are being bombarded with neutrons. If these are of all kinds of speeds, some of the 235 nuclei will be fissioned, mostly by neutrons that have been slowed down by impact, and a few of the 238 by some of the fastest neutrons. However, so large a proportion of the neutrons will be absorbed by 238 nuclei, without fission (that is, without production of fresh neutrons), that the reaction will not propagate itself —it will die out like a fire with an insufficient supply of oxygen. If, however, all, or nearly all, the neutrons are of thermal energy they will be very effective in producing fission of the 235's and, since the 238's are completely indifferent to them, can go bumping round until (except for a proportion that meet impurities or escape at the surface of the whole assembly) they fission a 235, although the proportion of 235's is small. Thermal neutrons, then, give a possible way of producing a wholesale chain reaction with ordinary uranium, although the main constituent, uranium 238, is such an effective absorber of neutrons of moderate energy. But it takes many impacts to reduce the velocity of a neutron, and while these are going on, some of the neutrons will be absorbed by 238's, giving plutonium.

As regards thermalizing the neutrons, it has already been pointed out that the speed of fast neutrons can be reduced by collision with light nuclei, for instance, those of the hydrogen in paraffin wax. The nuclei of ordinary hydrogen —that is, protons—combine easily with neutrons, forming heavy hydrogen and, incidentally, giving out gamma rays. On this account hydrogen compounds are not suitable for slowing down neutrons when it is important to have as many of them as possible, although quite effective in Fermi's fundamental experiments, where the number of slow neutrons did not particularly matter. Heavy hydrogen nuclei, however, are very bad absorbers of neutrons, and so are certain other light atoms—helium, beryllium, carbon, and oxygen. When it comes to large-scale control, helium is out of the question, as it does not form solid compounds. The elements best suited to act as moderators, the name which is given to substances that reduce effectively the velocity of neutrons, are heavy hydrogen, in the form of heavy water, and carbon, in the form of graphite, which must be very pure. Heavy water is prepared by prolonged electrolysis, involving the extensive use of electric power, which is particularly cheap in Norway, on account of the abundant water power there available. The great commando raids carried out in the winter of 1942 against the heavy-water plant in Norway, where a hundred gallons or so of heavy water had been produced, were designed to prevent the Germans using it as a moderator. Elaborate and desperate raids to safeguard what seemed then to be a chemical curiosity rather than a weapon of war caused some bewilderment.

In planning a reactor involving neutron supply it is well, for control purposes, to have a substance that will absorb neutrons readily and so can be made to play the part of an air supply control in an ordinary furnace. Cadmium is a particularly strong absorber for all but very fast neutrons, and even then it absorbs to some extent: nucleus for nucleus it absorbs, in general, about a million times as effectively as the good non-absorber heavy hydrogen.

The first controlled nuclear reactor was constructed under Fermi's direction and, probably from the fact that in it uranium and graphite were piled together, was called a 'pile': all similar constructions have been so called since. A typical pile consists of uranium, enclosed in long aluminium tubes which are arranged in a lattice; a moderator, usually very pure graphite in the form of rods; and rods of cadmium which can be pushed in and out so as to control the number of neutrons careering about. Some of the neutrons are not released immediately a fission takes place, but come from radioactive fission products, and so are delayed. This makes control easier, just as it is much easier to control the temperature of a room where the effect of switching on heat is to produce a delayed warming than it would be if, the moment the heat were switched on, the temperature jumped.

Several things take place in a pile in which a controlled chain reaction is maintained. First of all, plutonium is produced in the uranium slugs from the plentiful isotope 238: this production was the ultimate object of the first pile set up in 1942. The uranium has to be removed at intervals in order to separate out by chemical processes the plutonium which has been formed: this is feasible because, having a different nuclear charge, it has different chemical properties, but is not particularly easy, as each ton of uranium contains only about a pound of plutonium. With the plutonium are produced various radioactive fission products, some of which have uses while others have to be disposed of so as to do no harm.

By exposing various elements to the intense neutron bombardment available in the pile radioactive isotopes, of many different kinds, can be produced. These have to-day extensive medical and biological uses, a word about which will be said later. The various radioactive changes are accompanied by the generation of intense gamma rays, which are both very dangerous and very penetrating. Every reactor, then, has to be surrounded by a thick protective wall, which also looks after any fast neutrons escaping.

The pile generates great heat, which has to be carried away by circulating a fluid through pipes which run through

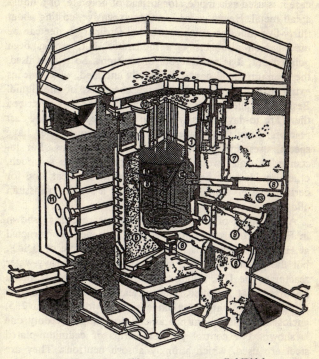

FIG. 7.   The Harwell heavy-water reactor, called 'Dido'

1. Aluminium tank containing heavy water
2. Level of heavy water
3. Fuel element
4. Experimental hole
5. Graphite reflector
6. Experimental hole
7. Water-cooled thermal shield
8. Experimental hole containing heavy water
9. Experimental hole containing graphite
10. Vertical experimental hole
11. Columns of graphite to provide beams of thermal neutrons
12. One of six control arms
13. Concrete shield

(From *Atomic Energy Research at Harwell*, by permission of United Kingdom Atomic Energy Authority and Butterworth's Publications Ltd.)

it. This fluid may be air (a fluid is anything that flows and need not be a liquid), or it may be heavy water, in which case it is used as a moderator instead of graphite, or a liquid alkali metal. Heavy water is rather expensive, costing about thirty-five times as much as whisky. Ordinary water can be used, which also acts as a moderator, but, as has been pointed out, it is an absorber of neutrons. So if it is used, the uranium metal has to be heavily enriched, which means extra cost that makes up for the cheapness of the liquid. Besides the piles which use moderators in the way described there are to-day others which do not. They are called fast reactors, since they make use of fast neutrons. They have special uses and present many special problems. For instance, as water would slow down the neutrons so much, other liquids must be used to carry away the heat, and for certain reasons liquid sodium metal or a sodium-potassium alloy are often used.

An example of a heavy-water nuclear reactor is shown in Fig. 7. This represents one which has been constructed at Harwell, where it is known by the nickname of 'Dido', but the general design is similar to that of a heavy-water reactor at the U.S. Atomic Energy Commission's National Laboratory at Argonne. The nuclear fuel element consists of rods of ordinary uranium enriched with uranium 235, enclosed in aluminium containers: for simplicity only one is shown. For control purposes strips of cadmium-plated steel are used, which strongly absorb neutrons. They are lowered and withdrawn like the arms of railway signals. Again, for simplicity, only one is shown. The heavy water is contained in the central tank, into which fuel elements and control arms protrude. It is used both as moderator and as cooling agent, being circulated through a system where the heat is withdrawn. Heavy water is, as said, very expensive, but this particular reactor is designed for research and development purposes.

When it comes to using nuclear power for industrial purposes the heat, however extracted, can be used for generating steam, which will run turbines attached to dynamos in the ordinary way. Possibly, in the future, other ways of converting the heat energy into electrical energy may be found. As a source of power the nuclear reactor has the advantage that the weight of fuel is exceedingly small, the disadvantage that it is very costly and that careful protection against the unpleasant penetrating radiations is needed, and further that, from time to time, radioactive waste has to be disposed of. Nevertheless, the Americans had already produced in 1954 a submarine thermal reactor prototype and probably by now a submarine engined by it is in service.

So much for the large-scale nuclear reactor, which may have a great future as a generator of heat for power production. At present its chief use is to produce new elements. Plutonium we shall have to consider again when the atomic bomb is in question. The artificial radioactive isotopes have more peaceful uses. The export, to all parts of the world, of such isotopes is a rapidly increasing activity at Harwell and exceeds a thousand shipments—using the term to include airships—monthly. When isotopes of short life are in question air transport is, of course, the only practicable method. An interesting sidelight is that they are often carried in the wing-tips, since, if they emit penetrating gamma rays, this distance from passengers and crew make them harmless without the need for thick and heavy lead containers.

The particular advantage of radioactive isotopes is that they behave chemically like the normal stable atoms, but can be followed by their physical activity: they are ticketed or labelled atoms. Perhaps they can be compared to marked coins or notes, used to trace the wanderings of a particular batch of money: for all purchasing purposes they behave exactly as ordinary currency, but they can be recognized by the expert. The birds marked by a small ring, to study problems of migration, may offer an even closer analogy.

Let us take a simple example, carbon. Ordinary carbon consists of 98.9 per cent of atoms of mass 12 and 1.1 per cent of atoms of mass 13, both, of course, stable. But an isotope of mass 14 can be prepared by irradiating nitrogen with neutrons. This is radioactive, giving out an electron: it breaks down very slowly, the half life being 5568 years. Slow break-down means feeble activity, but with modern methods of detection this is not a serious difficulty. If, now, a carbon compound is made in which a proportion of the atoms are carbon 14, and it is given as a food to animals, or supplied to plants in the air or in the soil, the fate of that particular compound can be followed. A sample of blood may, for instance, be removed and tested for the carbon. Or labelled carbon may be introduced into the carbon dioxide surrounding a plant and its incorporation in the plant followed. An indication of the activity in this field is that several hundred different compounds labelled with carbon 14 can now be purchased. The slow rate of break-down means that they can be kept in stock, which is, of course, not true of rapidly disintegrating isotopes.

Carbon is a good example because there is another radioactive isotope, carbon 11, prepared by bombarding boron with fast deuterons from cyclotrons and such-like accelerators. This has a half life of 20 minutes, which means that it is very active, but must be used promptly: after some hours there is not much of it left.

Again, the stable isotope, as against the unstable isotope, may be used as a tracer. For this purpose carbon must be prepared with a proportion of carbon 13 much larger than that normally present. The carbon 13 has then to be detected by an instrument of the general type of Aston's mass spectrograph, which is a slower and more troublesome method than a measurement of radioactivity. Other stable isotopes, in particular heavy water, can be used to follow the course of chemical actions in the body or in the plant.

Radio-phosphorus, mass 32 instead of the normal stable mass 31, is extensively used: it gives out electrons of moderate energy and has a convenient half life of 14.3 days, which means fair activity and no need for undue haste lest your sample shall have mostly changed into inactive sulphur its ultimate fate. It may be administered as a phosphate and has been used to demonstrate, among other things, the astonishing rapidity with which the phosphorus taken up i food passes into the bone. It is selectively absorbed in leukaemic cells, where its radiations have a beneficial action: in fact it has been used therapeutically with very striking results. It, too, has been much used in botanical investigations.

Iodine also has proved to be very important both for medical investigation and for medical treatment. There are many radio-isotopes: that of mass 131 has a convenient half life of 8 days, giving out electrons and gamma rays. Thanks to the gamma rays its presence in the body can be detected without the need of cutting out tissue or removing blood. It passes, for instance, into the thyroid gland and its presence can then be shown by holding a Geiger counter against the neck. In this way the percentage of the administered iodine, the time taken for it to arrive, and the length of its life in the thyroid can all be determined. This is very important: for instance, if a patient has an over-active thyroid gland it will take up more iodine, and do this more rapidly, than will a normal gland. The therapeutic uses are also considerable.

There are many other radio-isotopes in active use. A radio-isotope of iron, with a half life of 47 days, is extensively employed in investigating the behaviour of blood cells. Two useful isotopes of iron, prepared with the cyclotron, are used for therapy, especially in cases of leukaemia. Needles of radioactive cobalt, which emit gamma rays of a particularly uniform penetration, are used in place of the old 'radium needles' in the treatment of cancer. A new branch of physical medicine has grown up in a few years.

There is an application of radioactive isotopes manufactured not by man, but by nature, which is of strange interest, namely to find the age of objects some thousands of years old—the so-called radio-carbon dating. Neutrons are produced by cosmic rays, the process taking place most vigorously at heights of some 50,000 feet. These neutrons react with nitrogen nuclei, expelling a proton and producing the active carbon isotope 14, to which reference has just been made. The carbon 14 atoms oxidize—we should say 'burn' if there were millions of millions of millions of them together, as in a grain of coke dust—to carbon dioxide, which gets blown about and stirred up with the lower atmosphere. Eventually it is taken up by plants, just like ordinary carbon dioxide, from which it is chemically indistinguishable, and the carbon 14 is built into their structure with the normal carbon.

The carbon in animals comes from eating vegetation, so that all living things have a small proportion of the radiocarbon in them. Very little, for there is very little of the radioactive element about: it is created very slowly and there is a balance between the creation and decay which prevents it accumulating. The resulting figure is about 80 tons of radio-carbon on the surface of the earth. If this sounds a respectable amount, divide it by the 200 million square miles of the earth's surface and visualize a square mile. An ounce of normal wood carbon gives about 43 disintegrations a minute.

As long as the plant is living it replenishes its carbon from the air and builds into itself the normal very small amount of radio-carbon. But at death the supply of fresh carbon stops, while the radio-carbon already there decays with the half life period 5568 years. The proportion of active carbon to normal carbon, then, steadily diminishes after death. Thus carbon from the mummy of a man dead about 5500 years should show, per gram, about half the activity of carbon from a recently dead animal or tree.

The principle of radio-carbon dating is, then, simple—it is only necessary to find the proportion of radio-carbon in carbon from old wood or old bones to learn the time that has elapsed since the tree was cut down or the animal died. The practice is not so simple, on account of the small number of disintegrations and the background of odd disturbing disintegrations due to cosmic radiation and chance traces of radioactive material. It has, however, been developed to a method of considerable reliability by W. F. Libby and his school. The general correctness of the results has been checked by such things as wood taken from between old growth-rings of a recently dead sequoia tree, count of the rings giving the date when they were built up. Thus in one such case the growth-rings gave an age of 1377 and the radio-carbon method 1430 years, a difference of an odd fifty years not being serious with so great an age. Such things as wood from ancient Egyptian ships and coffins, charcoal from neolithic villages, rope sandals and bones from caves, of ages from 2000 to 11,000 years or so, have been dated by the radio-carbon method, and, with the perfecting of the method, this range will probably be extended.

We now turn to the nuclear bomb, and here a factor that has not been mentioned, that of size of the mass of fissionable material, is of great importance. Neutrons, even in an absorbing substance like uranium 235, have a long path, and so, if we are dealing with a small lump of the substance, say the size of a golf ball, a large proportion of them will depart through the surface without producing any effect and there will not be enough left to produce a chain reaction. The larger the lump, the less surface there will be per unit of volume: when the diameter of a sphere is doubled the volume is increased by 8 times and the surface by only 4 times, and if the diameter is trebled the volume is made 27 times as great and the surface only 9 times. The consequence is that, while in a large lump of uranium 235 or plutonium the reaction runs away like an avalanche and there is an explosion, in a small lump too many neutrons are lost without producing fission for this to occur.

In a nuclear bomb we must use a fast neutron reaction, because first of all material added as a moderator would increase the size and weight of the bomb but, more fundamental, the slowing down of the reaction, though only by millionths of a second, would considerably decrease the effectiveness of the bomb. For various reasons the only materials suitable for a rapid chain reaction are uranium 235 and plutonium. A lump of either below a certain critical size is safe: above the critical size it detonates, for there are always enough stray neutrons about, owing to cosmic-ray effects, to provoke the avalanche, since the fission of even one suitably placed nucleus will start the whole chain reaction. The fission bomb, then, consists of two or more pieces, each below the critical size, which, when the bomb is required to explode, are automatically and very swiftly brought together by a special mechanism which can be set to go into action at the desired instant. As soon as contact is made between the different pieces the whole assembly goes off. As a further refinement the bomb is surrounded by a wall of material which reflects back a proportion of the neutrons which would normally escape without performing their task of fissioning and further, by its inertia, hinders a too early expansion.

Plutonium, as we have seen, can be prepared from uranium 238 in the pile and chemically separated. Uranium 235 cannot, however, be chemically separated from 238, because both have the same chemical properties. Advantage, therefore, has to be taken of the difference of physical properties due to the difference of mass and this is made more difficult because the relative difference of mass is so small. Any mass spectrograph, of Aston type, relying upon the joint effect of electric and magnetic fields to separate particles of different mass, could clearly be used, and such devices, on an enormous scale, have been applied. The method generally used for the separation is, however, that of diffusion.

In any gas at a particular temperature the average energy of motion of all the molecules is the same. This means, of course, that in a gas that is a mixture of molecules of different mass the lighter ones have, on the whole, a greater velocity than the heavier. In a gaseous mixture of isotopes, therefore, when diffusion processes are in question, such as the passage through very small holes in a porous barrier, the lighter particles will pass through more rapidly than the heavier ones and there will be a partial separation.

To apply the method to the isotopes of uranium they must be prepared in gaseous form, which means that they must be combined with some other element to give molecules which do not readily adhere on one another, just as carbon can be carried in gaseous form by combining it with oxygen to make carbon dioxide. The most suitable compound is uranium hexafluoride: this is, it is true, a solid at ordinary temperatures, but it is easily vaporized. Fluorine is a light element, of one isotope only, but even so the difference of mass of the two isotopic hexafluorides is just under 0.9 per cent, which means that the difference of average velocities is less than one-half per cent. The differentiation by diffusion is therefore extremely slow and demands repeated stages, in cascade, if a substantial separation is to be effected.

The separation of uranium 235 in pound weight quantities, originally undertaken at Oak Ridge, was therefore a prodigious operation. The manufacture of suitable porous walls, which are somewhat of the nature of sheets of unglazed 'biscuit' porcelain, was alone a formidable undertaking. Hundreds of acres of such porous plate are incorporated in the plant, which itself covers acres and contains thousands of miles of piping and thousands of pumps. The cost of a pound of uranium 235 must make platinum look like worthless rubbish.

The atomic bomb dropped at Hiroshima was of uranium 235: how much has not been made public, but probably some tens of pounds in weight. Complete fission cannot have taken place and two pounds' weight of pure 235, if completely fissioned, would have produced the explosive effect observed, given as equivalent to that of 20,000 tons of T.N.T. Progress in this pleasant field has been so rapid that this is now regarded as a contemptible catastrophe. The two bombs dropped at Bikini in 1946 were more powerful, and that exploded at Eniwetok in 1948 is said to have had six times the power of the Hiroshima bomb. But these effects have been dwarfed by a quite different type of bomb that has been developed. In this the energy is released by building light nuclei together to form heavier ones—fusion instead of fission, the left-hand side of Fig. 5 instead of the right.

The greatest energy would be developed by putting four hydrogen nuclei together to make a helium nucleus, a process which would lead to a disappearance of nearly one per cent of the mass. This build-up is now believed to occur in the sun and other stars—for, in the universe, our sun ranks as a small star. The process, however, is not a direct one but, according to Bethe, takes place in six stages at temperatures of tens of millions of degrees. It may be of interest here to look back to 1903 and to quote, as an example of the foresight of genius, what Rutherford and Soddy then wrote. 'The energy latent in the atom must be enormous compared with that rendered free in ordinary chemical change. . . . Hence there is no reason to assume that this enormous store of energy is possessed by the radio-elements alone. . . . The maintenance of solar energy, for example, no longer presents any fundamental difficulty if the internal energy of the component elements is considered to be available, i.e. if the processes of sub-atomic change are going on.'

We are not likely to be able to mimic the stellar chain of events on earth, but temperatures of the magnitude in question are momentarily created in fission bomb explosions. At such temperatures the energy of motion of the nuclei is sufficient to give them a good probability of penetrating the potential barrier and so forming compound nuclei. In fusion, as against fission, the energy of motion is the agent for spreading nuclear reactions. Reactions promoted by the colossal thermal velocities at temperatures of millions of degrees go by the name of thermo-nuclear reactions.

There are theoretical reasons for supposing that particular hydrogen isotopes can be made to combine in a thermo-nuclear reaction: a mixture of deuterium and tritium should be 'fusible'. In 1952 the Americans exploded at Eniwetok—a small island in the Pacific that never lent its name, as Bikini did, to a rudimentary garment—a thermo-nuclear bomb that is believed to have consisted of liquid deuterium and tritium, incorporated with a fission-process bomb to generate the necessary temperature. The hydrogen isotopes have to be in the liquid state to get the atoms into the necessary closeness and this, on account of the exceedingly low temperatures needed for liquefaction, means considerable refrigerating apparatus. This bomb, then, was a purely experimental, and not a droppable, prototype.

In 1953, however, the Americans detected in the upper atmosphere atomic fragments which, with other evidence, gave strong reason to believe that the Russians had detonated in Siberia a thermo-nuclear bomb containing heavy hydrogen and the light element lithium, of atomic number 3, in the form of a compound, lithium deuteride. Great advantages, from the point of view of easy devastation, are that no refrigerating plant is necessary and that the compound is relatively cheap. Tritium is very difficult to make in any quantity and so is prodigiously expensive: it is said to cost a million dollars a pound. Within a year the Americans let off a lithium-deuteride bomb at Eniwetok.

We are therefore at a fresh stage of atomic destruction. The original Hiroshima bomb was, as has been noted, marked as the equivalent of 20,000 tons of T.N.T. It is said that a thermo-nuclear fusion bomb equivalent to a thousand times this has already been let off, and by the time that this is printed that figure may well have been exceeded. This is no place to discuss the moral and social problems so created. The work which started the astonishing mental chain reactions that culminated in this ill-omened exploit was carried out, at the time when the writer was a research student, with the light-hearted enthusiasm shown by expert billiard players at the game of their choice. So far two acts of the drama have been played. Let us hope that the third act does not disclose that it is a world tragedy that we have been witnessing.

# CHAPTER XI

# Uncertainty

THE great Dutch physicist Kamerlingh Onnes said that over the door of every physics laboratory should be set the motto *Door meten tot weten* ('Through measurement to knowledge'). It is true that every great advance in the exact sciences, physics and astronomy in particular, has been made as a result of measurement, measurement becoming ever more accurate and more accurate. The theory of relativity arose because of the results of extremely precise optical measurements. Modern theories of the structure of the atom are based on exact measurements of the behaviour of particles and on such things as the minutely determined position of spectral lines. Our views on the structure of the universe and its history are founded on the laborious measurements made with spectrometers and with telescopes that give angular positions with the greatest precision. So it has always been. Kepler was led to find the true forms of planetary orbits as a result of small discrepancies between the observed positions of Mars and those computed on the older theories,[1] and the triumph of Newton's great theory of universal gravitation was that it led to Kepler's laws.

[1] The greatest difference between the position of Mars as determined by the observations of the time and as calculated on the old theory of epicyclic orbits was 8 minutes of arc, which is about the angular distance between the two sides of an ordinary pencil as seen from a distance of 10 feet. 'From

Inventive amateurs who conjure up, from fancy, theories of the universe and of the atom, and of things between, often forget that agreement with measurements is the hard test that every trained disciple of the exact sciences applies. 'If what you say is true, how do you account for the position of that spectral line, or the velocity of that particle, or the temperature at that point, which is absolutely fundamental for the problem?' is the question which the expert puts to the ingenious paradoxer, only to be told, as a rule, that that is for the expert to find out. Where there is no quantitative law there can be no check.

The only things that are permanent are the experimental results. That is the lesson of the history of science. However well supported the theories may seem to be, they may not last. Let us consider the ether of space, which, when the writer was a student—happy days! *O fortunatos nimium, sua si bona norint*[2]—dominated theoretical physics. Lord Kelvin was then still one of the great figures in science and he, lecturing at Philadelphia, under the auspices of the Franklin Institute, on the Wave Theory of Light, had said, 'You can imagine particles of something, the thing whose motion constitutes light. This thing we call the luminiferous ether. This is the only substance we are confident of in dynamics. One thing we are sure of, and that is the reality and substantiality of the luminiferous ether'; and, still more precisely, 'You may regard the existence of the luminiferous ether as a reality of science; that is, we have an all-pervading medium, an elastic solid, with a great degree of rigidity—a rigidity so prodigious in proportion to its density that the vibrations of light in it have the frequencies I have mentioned'. The luminiferous ether of which he spoke is no more. Henri Poincaré, the greatest mathematician and one of the acutest minds of his generation (he died in 1912), wrote, 'Les gens du monde sont frappés de voir combien les théories sci-

these eight minutes', wrote Kepler, 'we will construct a new theory that will explain the motions of all the planets.'

[2] 'Too happy they, if they only knew their good fortune.'

entifiques sont éphémères' ('Men of the world are struck by the speed with which scientific theories pass'). Nothing has happened since his death to cause us to revise this statement. E. A. Milne, one of the greatest figures in the modern theory of the structure of the universe, went so far as to say that a book by a physicist on a physical theory was usually quite out of date in ten years' time.

The experiments and observations tell us how the machine of Nature works. They tell us about the measurable behaviour of things that can be weighed and measured. The theories give us, as has already been pointed out, a scheme which ties together large numbers of observations. This is not a particularly modern point of view. Osiander wrote the preface to the book *De Revolutionibus* of Copernicus, which appeared in 1543 when the author was on his deathbed, and there he says that the object of an astronomer is to put together the history of the celestial motions from diligent and careful observation and then to think out the causes of these motions or, if he cannot find the real causes, to devise hypotheses which, if accepted, will allow the motions, in the future as in the past, to be calculated on geometrical principles. And, he continues, it is not even necessary that these hypotheses shall be true or indeed probable: one thing alone suffices, that calculations founded on them shall agree with observation.

Nothing could be clearer than that, which embodies the modern point of view, a point of view emphasized by one who said paradoxically that the Inquisition and Galileo agreed on one point only, that there was a perfectly definite question to be answered, as to whether the sun or the earth was at rest, and that there they were both wrong. For on the theory of relativity the sun is no more a centre of absolute rest than is the earth and the whole system of the planets could be worked out just as correctly starting from the supposition that the earth was at rest. It so happens that, owing to the immense mass of the sun, the mathematics is much simpler, much more convenient if the sun be taken as at rest, but we know that, even considering a framework supplied by the so-called fixed stars, it is not.

Very well, then, our scientific theories are working hypotheses, makeshifts to enable us to accomplish the next advance in measuring, and in making rules which the measured quantities obey. Is there, then, nothing real but weighed and measured quantities, or weighable and measurable quantities? Must we, then, attempt to explain everything in terms of the weighable and the measurable? No, would answer the majority of men and women. But many of this majority would not realize that they had reason on their side, reason and great reasoners, especially men like Eddington, Milne, Whittaker, and Planck, who have contributed so much to the most intricate, the most difficult-to-understand parts of the science of modern cosmology and of physics. Let us look at this very difficult question.

Physical science deals with things that can be weighed and measured, but this clearly does not mean the whole of reality. The methods of science imply a choice and an abstraction. As regards choice, the whole history of science has been at every stage governed by what has been selected for measurement and by the decision as to how much time and care should be devoted to perfecting methods of measuring one thing rather than another, and this is a human and personal question. There was no law that made Rutherford choose to study alpha rays rather than, say, the mechanical strength of solids, which is a mine of unsolved mysteries. Again, it so happened that experimental optics had taken a turn which had made, by the end of the nineteenth century, the measurement of the wave-length of spectral lines a matter of the highest accuracy: the intensity of the spectral lines, however, was a subject to which relatively little attention had been given, and here the determinations were rough. Now Bohr's original theory was invented to explain relations between spectral wave-lengths and accepted because it accounted precisely for several very accurately established relations in this field. It could say, however, very little about intensities, and if agreement here had been the experimental test the theory would probably never have been put forward. The material world displays an infinite field for experiment and speculation; a drop of water, a grain of sand offer problems that could occupy the greatest brain for a lifetime. What we find, what we think important, is determined by choice. What determines that choice?

Another aspect of this question is what I have called abstraction. Here is a lump of copper. I give it to a physicist and ask him to find out all about it. Probably, after long sessions in the laboratory, he tells me the density, the conductivity for heat and electricity, the specific heat, the elasticity, and many other such properties of the metal of the lump, and if I said that I wanted to know more he might, together with the team he had by now assembled, find out the way in which all these quantities varied with the temperature and the pressure, and investigate the behaviour of the molten metal. Pressed for more, he and his hundred or thousand helpers might study the way the metal behaves under large forces, prepare it in crystalline form, and start all over again measuring the properties of the single crystal. By this time they have brought in specialists in magnetism who measure the magnetic properties in every variety of circumstances they can think of. I am presented with all the results and told that that is getting on for all about the copper.

But if I give it to a chemist he will probably first of all supply me with an exact analysis of the metal, giving the impurities which always exist, either as a few parts in a hundred or a few parts in a million. He and his team will study all the salts that can be prepared from it, organic and inorganic. His physical chemical colleagues will measure the electro-chemical potentials, the surface properties of various kinds, the ionic mobilities, and what not. All about the copper would now have quite a different aspect. Different again would be the engineer's report, the geologist's report, and so on. Of course, if I asked a business man about it, he would give me the market price, and if I replied that that was not an aspect of reality about the copper, he would doubt my sanity. And it *is* an aspect of reality. It is a figure, a numerical aspect of a reality that to many men, who are also realities, is extremely important.

But let me go further. Suppose I had given the lump of copper to the painter Rembrandt. The play of light on the surface—polarized by reflexion, says the physicist, very truly —slightly oxidized, says the chemist, quite correctly—would probably have been the thing about the copper that interested him, and if he had nothing else to do he might have painted it in a variety of circumstances: against a velvet curtain, at dusk, and who knows how. Is not the play of light on the surface of the copper, as perceived by the artist, a reality? All the properties mentioned, and many others, are aspects of the reality that make up the copper. Science abstracts aspects of the reality that can be measured, but even the scientist leaves a multitude of aspects unmeasured and is always bound to do so. Twenty years ago he could not have measured the behaviour of the copper to radiations of many kinds accessible to-day: are we to suppose that the next twenty years will reveal no new properties?

Science, then, attempts an accurate description, in terms of current theories which admittedly are makeshifts, of a part of the mechanical side of Nature, a part selected more or less arbitrarily under the influence of the available instruments and methods of experiment and the mental disposition of the great leaders of research. I cannot affirm with certainty that the point of view which has been presented here would be accepted by every man of science, but it has been reached by some of the greatest minds in modern science and has, for instance, been summarized by Eddington when he wrote, 'We have acknowledged that the entities of physics can from their very nature form only a partial aspect of reality'. Planck, who changed the whole aspect of physics, who, in a sense, created modern theoretical physics, was far from believing that science tells us all, or can tell us all, about the real world: he said that the observations that we make do not form the physical world, but that they only bring us messages from another world which lies behind them and which is independent of them, that there exists a real external world of which science gives us one aspect.

The great question to which so many men of science have ultimately turned, and on which they have expressed so many differences of opinion, is that of causality. Even to define exactly what is meant by causality is not easy,[3] but, roughly speaking, the question is whether what we observe happens because of some law behind everything or whether, in the end, everything is governed by pure chance. Often things that are called chance events are not, in the real sense, chance events to the physicist. The roulette wheel is spun and comes to rest in a particular position, ordinarily called a chance position, but if we knew the exact twist given to the wheel originally and all the frictional forces concerned we should be able to calculate—to a good degree of approximation, but not with the highest precision, on account of the kind of molecular fluctuations considered when the Brownian movement was discussed—the position in which it would stop. The same is true of the spin of a coin. Or take a more difficult question, in radioactivity. Of a million atoms of radium we know approximately what proportion will disintegrate in a given time interval, a question of chance, of probability. But if we consider any particular atom, there is no way of calculating when it will break up and expel a particle. Is there a cause or is it pure chance? The first example, the roulette wheel, shows that on account of molecular vibrations, governed by probability laws, we can never predict a physical fact exactly; the second shows that in some cases we cannot predict it at all.

Before the coming of modern physics it was possible to take a simple and extreme view of this problem from the scientific point of view. Laplace, the great mathematician and astronomer who said—and it is as true to-day as when he said it—'Ce que nous connaissons est peu de chose, ce

[3] The word represented by 'cause' has sixty-four meanings in Plato and forty-eight in Aristotle.

que nous ignorons est immense'[4]—put forward the view that an intelligence which should know the masses, positions, and velocities of every particle in the universe at one particular moment, and the forces between them, and should further have sufficient powers of calculation, would be able to embrace in one formula the movements of the mightiest bodies and of the lightest atoms, and so both foretell the whole future and trace back the whole past. This mathematical and mechanical mythology was at one time widely accepted in certain scientific circles: in fact a famous writer[5] of the end of the past century said that at that time a great majority of scientists were of this way of thinking. The thesis, pressed to extremes, is this: all matter, including the matter of the brain, which is the physical seat of our emotions and reasoning, is made up of material atoms: the behaviour of all atoms is governed by precise mechanical laws, so that the whole history of movement, chemical combination and, in fact, of all modifications of assemblages of matter is determined by mechanics: our thoughts, arising as a result of material combinations and changes in the brain, ultimately depend upon mechanical laws. Hence the whole future, both of thought and of the material universe, is ineluctably determined by the whole present. This is the extreme form of materialism, which, incidentally, implies determinism— that free will does not exist.

[4] 'What we know is a trifle, what we do not know is immense.' Most—if not all—great thinkers have realized this. Newton, who said in his old age, 'I do not know what I may appear to the world, but to myself I seem to have been only like a boy, playing on the sea-shore, and diverting myself in now and then finding a smoother pebble or a prettier shell than ordinary, whilst the great ocean of truth lay all undiscovered before me': Goethe, who put into the mouth of his Wagner, typifying the learned, pedantic fool, the words:

'Und wie wirs dann zuletzt so herrlich weit gebracht'
(And note to what a height our science has been brought)

only to be rebuked and ridiculed by Faust, the true scholar, who had all the wisdom of his time.
[5] Ernst Mach.

This general belief was not a new one when Laplace put it forward and supported it with his mighty authority. It is, in fact, comprised in a verse of Omar Khayyám's, written some seven hundred years earlier:

With Earth's first Clay They did the Last Man knead,
And then of the Last Harvest sow'd the Seed:
   And the first Morning of Creation wrote
What the last Dawn of Reckoning shall read.

What led Laplace to enunciate this scientific fatalism or determinism, to give it its philosophic name, was, no doubt, the prodigious success of the Newtonian scheme in explaining on the basis of the law of gravitational action between mass points the whole scheme of the universe, as then known. Newton himself was firmly opposed to materialism: he wrote specifically, 'This most beautiful System of the Sun, Planets and Comets could only proceed from the counsel and dominion of an intelligent and powerful Being. . . . This Being governs all things, not as the soul of the world, but as Lord over all', and much more to this effect. He had observed anomalies in the movements of Saturn and of Jupiter which he was unable to explain and was willing to admit that the correction of small irregularities might be in the hands of God. Laplace was able to account mathematically for all these irregularities on the basis of universal gravitation, which, no doubt, gave him supreme confidence in the mathematical method of prediction from a fundamental law. The story is well known of how Napoleon said to the great man, 'Monsieur Laplace, they tell me you have written this large book on the system of the universe and have never even mentioned its Creator', to which Laplace replied, 'Je n'avais pas besoin de cette hypothèse-là' ('I had no need of that hypothesis').

Every observed movement of the planets he had calculated from their past history—could not his Perfect Calculator, on the same basis, work out the totality of things from the complete description at one particular past instant. Other French materialists before Laplace had pictured man as a mechanical assemblage, in particular Offray de La Mettrie in his *L'Homme-machine,* in which, according to the English translation, '. . . a full detail is given of the several springs which move the human machine'. In fact the times just before the French Revolution, inspired with a jubilant confidence by the triumphs of exact science, probably saw the climax of materialism. There was a revival of this enthusiasm for the material as the basis of being and behaviour in the nineteenth century, when at one time the foundations of science appeared simple, solid, and sure. To-day, as we shall see, everything in science that served as the granite foundation of the materialist belief has faded to mist.

It is hard to think, as I write, that the movements of my pen were determined by the cosmical situation before the birth of our globe, but this is the logical conclusion from Laplace's supposition. The majority of men of science since the times of Laplace have been unwilling to accept the thesis, although slow to bring arguments against it. To-day there are no scientific arguments for it. But before passing to consider the modern position, it may be well to point out that, from the standpoint of the exact sciences, the arguments for Laplace's view were never very strong and his Perfect Calculator was of the same band as Eros and Venus, a personification of certain aspects of human idealism mixed with strong personal desires. Laplace's position in the history of science, as a great mathematician, astronomer, and physicist is, of course, as sure as ever. Only his philosophical faith is subject to criticism.

For what was Laplace's train of thought? Surely simply this. On the basis of a law that every single particle of matter attracts every other particle with a force proportional to the product of their masses and inversely as the square of their distance, and of Newton's three laws of motion, it is possible to calculate with great precision the movements of the planets, satellites, and comets, even, as I have recently shown, such perturbations of their motions as Newton was unable to explain. This method, then, is clearly one of enormous power. If it suffices to explain the observed motions, in all their details, of the planets, it will surely suffice to explain all motions and positions, and everything in the end must come down to motions and positions of ultimate particles. But this last sentence contains two enormous assumptions. The history of science is full of examples of the danger of extending the range of laws which have proved completely satisfactory in a certain field to regions far outside that field. To attempt to apply the laws of thermodynamics, verified so brilliantly where large-scale happenings are concerned, to the Brownian motion; to attempt to apply Maxwell's theory of gases to radioactive atoms; to attempt to apply the laws of heat, as known and so widely verified in the nineteenth century, to liquid helium, would, in each case, prove futile. It is a matter, perhaps, of detail rather than of principle that spiral nebulae are now held to be bodies a million times larger than that imagined by Laplace as the origin of the solar system. There is, in fact, today no generally accepted theory of the evolution of our cosy little group of planets. Why, then, speaking entirely from the standpoint of emotionless science, should it be reasonable to expect laws which have been verified in a limited, if large, field, to apply in a field quite different in kind?

All this is apart from the fundamental difficulty emphasized by Sherrington in the title of his great book *Man on His Nature*, apart, that is, from the paradox that we are part of what we are examining, at once inside and outside the field of study. In the drama of life we are both spectators and actors. Sherrington, the greatest physiologist of his time, the man who investigated with surpassing skill and interpretative genius the mechanism of bodily action, concluded his book with the words, 'We have, because human, an inalienable prerogative of responsibility, which we cannot devolve, no, not as once was thought, even upon the stars. We can share it only with each other.' I quote Sherrington because he was not professedly a religious man and so had nothing but the scriptures of science to inspire him against materialism.

The certainties of Laplace's scheme and even of less extreme forms of materialism might well be, then, denied where human thought and human actions are concerned. It is pretty clear that most thinking men believe in free will rather than that all their actions are predetermined. It might, in the old days, still be possible to believe that every material happening was predetermined by material causes, to accept the doctrine of causality in the material sense. However, the findings of modern science have made that very difficult, if not impossible. When we have considered the present strange situation, do not let us be too certain that the basic hypotheses of science, the fundamentals of the scientific faith of those who have faith in these matters, as we know them at present, will never change. They have changed a good deal in the lifetime of the writer: he is not bold to suppose that with his death they will crystallize into stability.

Observing the paths of the planets is, however great the elaboration of the instruments, apparently a simple matter in principle. We have seen that light has a structure, and that in consequence the image of a point, formed by a lens or concave mirror, is not a point but a system of fringes. This, however, does not trouble the observer of planetary motions. He can fix the position of his object with extraordinary precision and he can now—applying the theory of relativity where necessary, as in the case of the planet Mercury, which moves with a very high velocity in the part of its orbit nearest the sun—predict by calculation the positions of the bodies of the solar system with like precision. This astronomical certainty, this obedience to rule, has had the most profound effect upon thought, and not only scientific thought: it is a standard argument against cosmic anarchy, as in Meredith's famous sonnet, where Lucifer, the angelic rebel against celestial control, looking at the heavens, observed how

Around the ancient track marched, rank on rank,
The army of unalterable law.

We have seen how, when we come to ultimate particles, the Newtonian laws, which at the beginning of the century were still accepted as universally valid, no longer hold. To account for the experimental results the quantum theory was elaborated and a brief account of some of its great successes has been given. It might, then, be supposed that, when it comes to the rule of law, no fundamental change had been made: that, while a set of laws different from the Newtonian laws had to be observed when dealing with ultimate particles, the same type of certainty prevailed in this new world. Less precision, it might be admitted, has so far been obtained but, with the perfection of new instruments, new methods, and new details of theory, an accuracy similar to that obtained in the investigation of the solar system might eventually be hoped for. Such is not the case, as was first emphasized by Heisenberg, in his so-called uncertainty principle.

This principle, briefly discussed in Chapter VII, asserts, in effect, that there are limits to the precision with which numerical values of properties such as position, velocity, energy, and so on can be assigned to a particle, and that this lack of precision is not due to imperfections of our methods of measurement or of our instruments, but is inherent. Limits of accuracy are matters of everyday experience. Nobody would dream of measuring the height of a man to within a thousandth of an inch. When this kind of precision is considered his height would depend upon whether he was lying down or standing, and, if standing, upon his precise attitude, upon the time of day, upon his breathing, and a dozen other factors. It might be said, therefore, that it was practically impossible to measure the height of a man to a thousandth of an inch, or, if that is disputed, say a millionth of an inch. It is, however, perhaps not logically impossible, unthinkably impossible. It is, however, inherently impossible to find out how a man behaves spontaneously in a sudden emergency by asking him to sit down and write an essay on the problem. The method of test, which involves consideration, cannot by its nature tell us of what happens when there is no consideration. This is more analogous to the fundamental problem in physics.

Suppose that we want to establish the position of an ultimate particle and for precision let us say an electron. We must illuminate it with some form of radiation and detect the radiation which it scatters, which it throws off. We are contemplating imaginary experiments, so that we can use any form of radiation that we like and consider any physically conceivable form of microscope or other measuring machine. It is inherent in any form of radiation that the image formed of a sharp point by any form of microscope is not a sharp point but a blurred pattern, and that the shorter the wave-length the more precisely can the position of this image of the sharp point be measured. A detailed discussion would not add substantially to this: the conclusion clearly is that we should illuminate our electron or other particle with a radiation of very short wave-length, gamma rays, and that by proceeding to the limit we can make our precision as great as we like.

We have seen, however, that when radiation of high frequency falls on an electron it behaves mechanically in some ways as if it were a particle of an energy given by $h$ times the frequency: it, in a sense, strikes the electron and bounces off with a diminished energy. The velocity and direction of the electron after the impact of the quantum will depend upon the direction of the wave packet after impact, of the wave particle that is to reveal the position of the electron. The consequence of this, not fully argued here, is that the velocity of the particle is indeterminate and that the more closely we fix the position, by using waves of very short length (which means a quantum of very high frequency and so of very high energy), the less closely do we know the velocity. In fact (indeterminacy of position) $\times$ (indeterminacy of momentum) is about equal to $h$, Planck's quantum constant. Attempting to observe the particle has knocked it off its course, and the more accurately we observe its position the more uncertain we are to how much its velocity has been disturbed. Observation means interference with what we are observing. We are reminded of G. K. Chesterton's old paradox, that we can never have a completely realistic stage play. The fourth wall of the room, say, represented on the stage has been taken away and a theatre full of people put in its place: it would not be natural for a man and wife, say, to behave as they are doing in the play when under the eyes of hundreds whom they know to be there. If we say that they do not know that they are being observed, then they are not behaving naturally, for anyone with normal senses would be aware of the spectators. Observation disturbs reality.

An indeterminacy similar to that of position and velocity runs through all our attempts to measure the properties of an ultimate particle. If we try to fix the exact time corresponding to an event we are uncertain as to the energy of the particle, and if we try to fix the exact energy we are uncertain as to the time, and once more the product of the two uncertainties multiplied is measured by Planck's constant. The paradox is a consequence of the duplicate nature of the particle and of the wave: each has a shot aspect, precise position, and a wave aspect, spread. If we concentrate on one, we neglect the other.

The trouble in understanding the position without mathematics is, of course, that we are trying to describe, in terms of the visible and tangible world, something which has no mechanical analogy in that visible and tangible world. The mathematics is not an explanation, but enables us to give a precise description, in terms of symbols, of the properties that are necessary, a precise description that involves an imprecision of interpretation. And this imprecision means that we cannot have a causal dependence of observable facts.

If it is not considered trifling with serious subjects, we may find a rough analogy in the duplicate nature of man, spiritual, or, if you prefer it, emotional, and material. For certain purposes an individual may be considered as entirely material: for transport in an aircraft he is just so much weight and those concerned with safe load are satisfied when they have weighed him. For other purposes, when, say, extreme examples of self-sacrifice are considered, weight and other material aspects, such as digestive processes, are not very relevant. For ordinary purposes we have to consider the co-existence of the two aspects, two aspects which, although they are necessary for description, are hard to reconcile and, in a sense, contradictory, in that a hundred or two pounds of living flesh and an angelic spirit are very dissimilar things. Sometimes one aspect is stressed, which accounts well for certain features of human behaviour, but gives a very in-definite and inadequate relation of the other: sometimes the other aspect is stressed, with a correspondingly unbalanced effect. Emphasis and exact description with reference to one means a corresponding neglect and vagueness with respect to the other.

This impossibility of determining exactly the state of a system composed of ultimate particles, however refined our methods, is agreed by all the leading physicists of to-day. As to its philosophical consequences there is a certain dif-ference of opinion, which adds to the general uncertainty. If Planck's definition is accepted, which says that an event is causally conditioned if it can be predicted with certainty, then we cannot, in the end, maintain that the principle of causality exists, since all that we can say in the ultimate is that there is a probability of a certain event following a cer-tain disposition of particles. Planck, in a way, tried to main-tain a kind of principle of causality by suggesting that it is possible to suppose an ideal mind which might be able to predict with certainty, but, he adds, 'we must forego making the ideal mind the object of a scientific investigation'. In other words, we can only maintain causality by foregoing science. This is the conclusion of the chief maker of modern physics, who stated quite plainly that the quantum of action, in which every physicist believes, set an insuperable limit to the accuracy of the physical measuring apparatus at our dis-posal. Max Born, another master of modern physical the-ory, takes exception to certain features of the views of

Planck and Einstein, but states quite plainly that a return to Newtonian determinism is impossible.

Again Schrödinger, the originator of wave mechanics, from which the uncertainty principle was derived, after describing the way in which Bohr and Heisenberg developed the theory, and admitting that it is widely accepted by prominent scientists, says that he himself cannot believe that the solution of the fundamental philosophic question as to the relation between subject and object, between perceiver and perceived, can ultimately depend upon 'the quantitative results of physical and chemical measurements with weighing scales, spectroscopes, microscopes, telescopes, with Geiger-Müller counters, Wilson chambers, photographic plates, arrangements for measuring the radioactive decay, and what not', and concludes that the observing mind is not a physical system. He further states that when we come to deal with smaller and smaller distances and shorter and shorter times no model based on our large-scale experiences can ever be valid: 'A completely satisfactory model of this type is not only practically inaccessible, but not even thinkable'.

Thus those great scientific minds which wish to maintain the principle of cause and effect, in which many believe innately, do so only by denying the universal validity of science. A consequence of this is that they are against scientific determinism. In their view the quantum theory, which some have hailed as restoring free will, has nothing whatever to do with the problem of free will. The physical concept of causality, like any other physical theory, has no bearing on ethical problems. Most men and women will probably agree that ethical problems have continuity: the history of science shows that physical theories undergo profound changes, and it may be assumed that they will continue to do so.

Enough has probably been said to indicate the kind of uncertainty that broods over the ultimate problems of science and the limits of their application to the ultimate problems of philosophy. The writer has no authority as a philosopher, but, in a sense, ability to develop philosophic themes in an academic manner is not in question. The point is that the findings of science do not contribute an element of certainty to problems that have vexed the minds of thinkers since antiquity, but rather the contrary. The materialist cannot find his supporters among those who are most skilled in modern physics and a few great names have been quoted to indicate that this statement is valid. As Goethe said: 'The greatest happiness of thinking man is to have searched into that which is open to his methods of research and to reverence in quietude that which is not open to these methods'.[6]

Belief in the magical powers of supernatural agencies, in mysterious forces uniting the macrocosm and the microcosm, the universe and man, has died away. The imaginary laws that united the mind and the fate of man with the operations of external nature are no longer sought: the invocations of Faust in his study, a representation of beliefs once valid in the learned world, no longer have any significance, except as a historic curiosity. The attitude of mind that made comets foretell the death of princes, that saw in the disposition of the planets at a man's birth an indication of his fate, that sought the cause of the movements of the heavenly bodies in a celestial harmony of which man was part, has vanished with the sacrifices to the gods and with the tributes to the shrine of Flora the passing of which Keats lamented.

In its place, however, has arisen in some quarters a mystical belief in the magical powers of science, a belief that precise measurement and prodigious calculation will lead not only to widespread human happiness, whose source the believers see in bigger and better refrigerators and in a more faithful record on a small screen of external happenings, but to a knowledge of ultimate reality, which the philoso-

---

[6] 'Das schönste Glück des denkenden Menschen ist, das Erforschliche erforscht zu haben und das Unerforschliche ruhig zu verehren.'—*Maximen und Reflexionen* (*zur Natur- und Wissenschaftslehre*). Nachlass. Jubiläumsausgabe, vol. 39, p. 100.

phers have vainly sought through the ages. Science tells us about the observable mechanism of nature: a closer study of the observable mechanism will lead, they devoutly trust, to a full knowledge of all that man should desire to know. They feel that material movements, of the kind revealed by instruments, govern all things. The latest lesson of the laboratory and study appears, however, to be that, while we can go very, very far in our study of the material world, there are mysteries that our methods can, by their very nature, never touch. Our science is a magnificent instrument for the purpose for which it was designed but not for all purposes, just as a modern calculating machine is a triumph of efficient ingenuity where complicated calculations are concerned, but will not construct, or help to understand, a Beethoven symphony, which is materially merely a matter of ordered vibrations.

Materialism, dialectical or otherwise, is a form of faith, founded on predilection and belief, which has an appeal for certain minds, but it certainly has no support from the findings or the founders of modern science.

# INDEX

# ANCHOR BOOKS